CLAMP

Tsubasa Volume 1

TRANSLATED AND ADAPTED BY Anthony Gerard

LETTERED BY Dana Hayward

Tsubasa Volume 2

TRANSLATED AND ADAPTED BY Anthony Gerard

LETTERED BY Dana Hayward

Tsubasa Volume 3

TRANSLATED AND ADAPTED BY William Flanagan

LETTERED BY Dana Hayward

A Del Rey® Book
Published by The Random House Publishing Group

Originally published in three separate volumes as:

Tsubasa, Volume 1. Copyright © 2004 by CLAMP
Tsubasa, Volume 2. Copyright © 2004 by CLAMP
Tsubasa, Volume 3. Copyright © 2004 by CLAMP

This 2007 edition published in the United States by Del Rey Books, an imprint of The Random House Publishing Group, a division of Random House, Inc., New York, and simultaneously in Canada by Random House of Canada Limited, Toronto. First published in Japan in serialization and subsequently published in book form by Kodansha Ltd., Tokyo, in 2003.

Del Rey is a registered trademark and the Del Rey colophon is a trademark of Random House, Inc.

ISBN-13: 978-0-307-29111-0
ISBN-10: 0-307-29111-1

Printed in the United States of America

10 9 8 7 6 5 4 3 2 1

Contents

TSUBASA

CLAMP

TRANSLATED AND ADAPTED BY
Anthony Gerard

LETTERED BY
Dana Hayward

Tsubasa Volume I crosses over with *xxxHOLiC* Volume I.
Although it isn't necessary to read *xxxHOLiC* to
understand the events in *Tsubasa*, you'll get to see the
same events from different perspectives if you read both!

Contents

Honorifics

Throughout the Del Rey Manga books, you will find Japanese honorifics left intact in the translations. For those not familiar with how the Japanese use honorifics, and more importantly, how they differ from American honorifics, we present this brief overview.

Politeness has always been a critical facet of Japanese culture. Ever since the feudal era, when Japan was a highly stratified society, use of honorifics—which can be defined as polite speech that indicates relationship or status—has played an essential role in the Japanese language. When addressing someone in Japanese, an honorific usually takes the form of a suffix attached to one's name (example: "Asuna-san"), or as a title at the end of one's name or in place of the name itself (example: "Negi-sensei," or simply "Sensei!").

Honorifics can be expressions of respect or endearment. In the context of manga and anime, honorifics give insight into the nature of the relationship between characters. Many translations into English leave out these important honorifics, and therefore distort the "feel" of the original Japanese. Because Japanese honorifics contain nuances that English honorifics lack, it is our policy at Del Rey not to translate them. Here, instead, is a guide to some of the honorifics you may encounter in Del Rey Manga.

-san: This is the most common honorific, and is equivalent to Mr., Miss, Ms., Mrs., etc. It is the all-purpose honorific and can be used in any situation where politeness is required.

-sama: This is one level higher than "-san." It is used to confer great respect.

-dono: This comes from the word "tono," which means "lord." It is even a higher level than "-sama," and confers utmost respect.

-kun: This suffix is used at the end of boys' names to express familiarity or endearment. It is also sometimes used by men among friends, or when addressing someone younger or of a lower station.

-chan: This is used to express endearment, mostly toward girls. It is also used for little boys, pets, and even among lovers. It gives a sense of childish cuteness.

Sempai: This title suggests that the addressee is one's "senior" in a group or organization. It is most often used in a school setting, where underclassmen refer to their upperclassmen as "sempai." It can also be used in the workplace, such as when a newer employee addresses an employee who has seniority in the company.

Kohai: This is the opposite of "-sempai," and is used toward underclassmen in school or newcomers in the workplace. It connotes that the addressee is of lower station.

Sensei: Literally meaning "one who has come before," this title is used for teachers, doctors, or masters of any profession or art.

[blank]: Usually forgotten in these lists, but perhaps the most significant difference between Japanese and English. The lack of honorific means that the speaker has permission to address the person in a very intimate way. Usually, only family, spouses, or very close friends have this kind of permission. Known as *yobisute*, it can be gratifying when someone who has earned the intimacy starts to call one by one's name without an honorific. But when that intimacy hasn't been earned, it can also be very insulting.

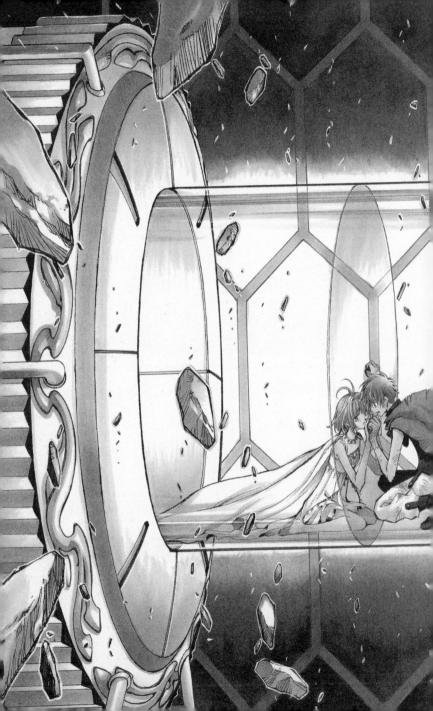

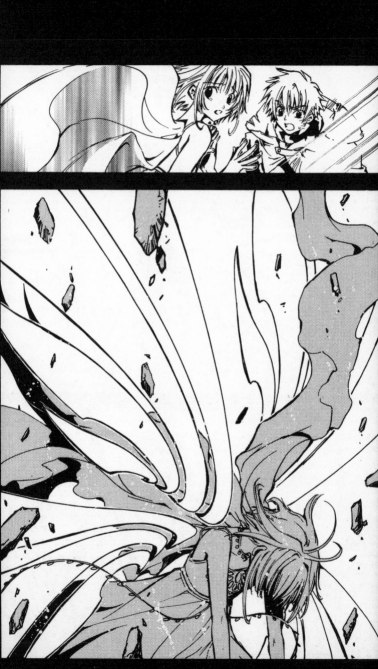

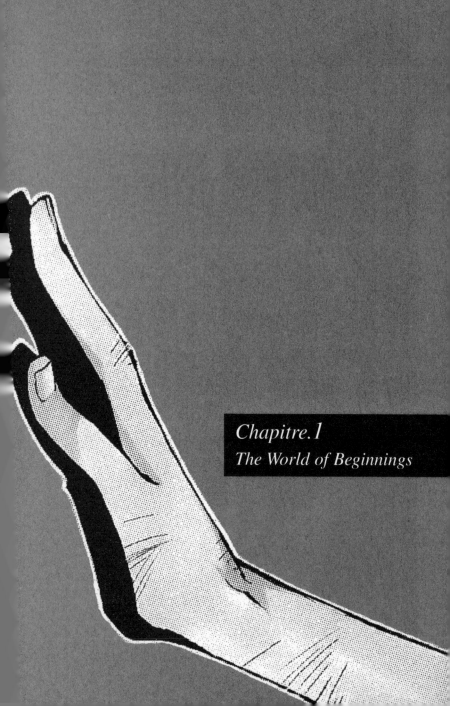

Chapitre.1
The World of Beginnings

HELLO, FATHER...

...I'M HOME.

JUST LIKE YOU THEORIZED, FATHER.

YOU WERE RIGHT. IN THIS COUNTRY THE RUINS YOU SEE ARE ONLY THE TIP OF LARGER STRUCTURES BURIED IN THE SAND.

BAM BAM

THE UNEARTHING OF THE EASTERN RUINS IS WELL UNDERWAY.

KA-CHAK

YES?

BAM BAM

14

HEH HEH HEH

BWIP

"SAKURA"!

S-

S-
SAKURA.

NICE TO BE BACK.

WHSPR ほの

WHSPR ぼの

I'M REALLY HAPPY THAT YOU'RE HOME.

SYAORAN.

...WHEN I WOULD BE COMING BACK.

YOUR HIGH-NESS KNEW—

SAKURA, YOU KNEW...

CHIPOK

GASP!

OH, I'M SORRY! I'M CUTTING OFF THE BLOOD TO YOUR LEGS!

15

MY BIG BROTHER IS THE KING, AND *HE'S* THE ONE WHO HAS TO LISTEN TO REPORTS!

AND YOU DON'T HAVE TO BE AT THE CASTLE NOW?

THE REST OF THE EXCAVATION TEAM CAME TO THE CASTLE TODAY.

YUP!

YOU DIDN'T— YOU DIDN'T COME BY YOURSELF, DID YOU?

AND IF THE EXCAVATION TEAM IS AT THE CASTLE...

...I WAS SURE THAT YOU WOULD BE COMING HOME!

TO REPORT ON THE SITUATION AT THE DIG.

BUT WE GREW UP TOGETHER, AND I DON'T HAVE MANY DEAR, DEAR FRIENDS LIKE YOU!

RIGHT ?

AND WHEN I TOLD THEM THAT I WANTED TO SEE YOU...

...MY BROTHER GOT ALL GRUMPY, LIKE *ALWAYS!*

HE DIED DURING THE DIG...

...BUT HIS LIFE WAS A HAPPY ONE.

HE WAS SMILING UNTIL THE LAST.

BESIDES, I CAN AFFORD TO LIVE ON MY OWN WITH THE MONEY FROM THE DIG.

BUT...

GRIP

WE INVITED YOU TO COME LIVE WITH US WHEN HE PASSED AWAY!

WHY DIDN'T YOU?

I WOULD HAVE FELT WEIRD LIVING IN A CASTLE.

IT'S NOT WEIRD! AFTER ALL, WE'VE BEEN FRIENDS SINCE WE WERE KIDS!

YOU'RE ROYALTY! I'M A COMMONER! COMMONERS CAN'T LIVE IN THE CASTLE!

19

ISN'T IT LONELY FOR YOU?

YOU'RE ALWAYS AT WORK. WE NEVER SEE EACH OTHER ANYMORE.

IT'S LONELY.

IT'S LONELY.

YOUR DEAREST DREAM.

YES, I KNOW.

BUT EXCAVATING THOSE RUINS WAS FOR BOTH ME AND MY DAD—

...I WONDER WHAT YOU'RE DOING AT THAT VERY MOMENT. I WONDER IF YOU EVER FIND TIME TO THINK OF ME A LITTLE.

WHEN I'M IN THE CASTLE AT NIGHT... WHEN IT'S TIME FOR BED...

I UNDER-STAND, BUT STILL...

...I MISS YOU WHEN YOU'RE GONE.

21

B-BMP B-BMP B-BMP B-BMP B-BMP

ARE YOU ALL RIGHT?

UHHHHHH.

JUST A LITTLE STARTLED.

BIIING BOOONG

I GUESS IT'S TIME FOR DINNER.

IT'S THE CASTLE BELLS.

.....

?

?

PURPOSE? WHAT PURPOSE?

SIGH

I HAVE THE FEELING MY BROTHER SET OFF THE BELL ON PURPOSE!

AND MY COUNTRY'S CITIZENS ARE ALL NICE PEOPLE!

THAT'S OKAY! YOU MUST BE TIRED FROM ALL YOUR WORK! IT'S ALL RIGHT. I CAN GET BACK ALONE.

WHEN THE BELL RINGS, IT MEANS I HAVE TO GO HOME.

OR BIG BROTHER WILL BE HERE TO GET ME!

NOTHING NOTHING

I'LL WALK YOU.

THANK YOU! IT LOOKS DELICIOUS!

YOUR FACE LOOKS FLUSHED.

TMP

OH, IT'S NOTHING!

YOUR HIGHNESS, WOULD YOU HAVE AN APPLE?

IT'S THE PRINCESS!

TMP TMP

GOOD EVENING!

YOUR HIGHNESS! GOOD EVENING!

RIGHT, FATHER?

...CAN NEVER BE.

THESE EMOTIONS I'M FEELING...

...BUT SHE'S STILL A PRINCESS.

WE MAY HAVE GROWN UP TOGETHER...

26

27

HE LISTENED TO THEIR ENTIRE REPORT.

RIGHT THERE ON HIS THRONE

THEN TÔYA GOT SELFISH AND SKIPPED OUT, RIGHT?

NO, I'M NOT *YOU!*

WHAT DID YOU SAY?!

AND SOON THEY'LL FINISH DIGGING THE WHOLE THING *UP!*

IT SEEMS SO, YOUR HIGH-NESS.

THEY'VE COME A LONG WAY ON THE DIG.

IT LOOKS LIKE THERE IS MORE TO THESE RUINS THAN WHAT IS ABOVE GROUND.

NO.

AND THE TWERP WILL BE BUSY FOR A

THE EXCAVATION WILL GO ON.

LONG

LONG

LONG

LONG

TIME TO COME.

STAB

STAB

STAB

GRIND

GRIND

HEH HEH

THEY'VE DISCOVERED A NEW UNDERGROUND PATH.

WHAT?!

I DON'T KNOW HOW FAR IT'S GOING TO TAKE THEM, BUT I'VE GIVEN PERMISSION TO CONTINUE DIGGING.

AND SO...

AND IF THERE'S SOME NEW RUIN, I'M SURE THAT'LL MAKE HIM THE HAPPIEST MAN ALIVE! SO IT'S *FINE WITH ME!!*

EEEEE

SYAORAN'S JUST LIKE HIS FATHER! HE LOVES RUINS AND HISTORY AND STUFF LIKE THAT!

TH-THAT'S JUST FINE WITH ME!

NORMALLY, ONE WOULDN'T EVEN BE ALLOWED TO *THINK* OF A COMMONER ASSOCIATING WITH ROYALTY.

TRUE.

AND TO THINK THAT SHE'S THE KINGDOM OF CLOW'S ONE-AND-ONLY PRINCESS AND THE FIRST IN LINE TO SUCCEED THE THRONE.

BUT YOUR SISTER, THE PRINCESS, IS SO CUTE, YOU JUST CAN'T HELP YOURSELF, CAN YOU?

I'M RIGHT, AREN'T I? ABOUT THAT?

HE'S DESTINED FOR HER.

BUT...

YES.

...THE ONE PRINCESS SAKURA IS DESTINED FOR.

SYAORAN IS...

...IT *REALLY* GETS ON MY NERVES!

YOUR PREDICTIONS OF THE FUTURE ARE NEVER WRONG.

AND THAT'S WHY...

HOWEVER...

...THE TWO OF THEM HAVE ADVERSITY WAITING AHEAD.

THE PRINCESS HAS AN UNUSUAL POWER.

I CAN'T SAY THAT I UNDERSTAND IT MYSELF.

ADVERSITY LIKE YOU'VE NEVER SEEN.

BUT I *CAN* SAY...

34

..... YES.

YES, BUT IT WILL COME OUT ALL RIGHT IF WE'RE THERE TO HELP HER.

YEAH, BUT IT'S THE "TWO OF THEM" PART THAT I DON'T LIKE.

AND...

...EVEN IF WE AREN'T THERE...

YOU NEVER GIVE UP...

...DO YOU, TÔYA?

...THE TWO OF THEM WILL COMBINE THEIR STRENGTHS TO FIGHT IT.

HONESTLY!!

STMP

スタ STMP

スタ STMP

MY BROTHER!!

HE NEVER STOPS TEASING ME!

IT'S BEAUTIFUL.

KREEE

SHP

AND BELOW IT, THERE'S SOMETHING MORE.

THAT'S WHEN I'LL TELL HIM.

I'VE GOT AN IDEA! I'LL BRING LUNCH TO HIM TOMORROW! AND AT LUNCHTIME WE CAN AT LEAST SPEND A LITTLE TIME TOGETHER!

SYAORAN WILL BE SO HAPPY TO HEAR IT!

36

THAT I...

...LOVE HIM.

JIING

EH?

JIING

IT'S PRETTY...

...AND A VERY CLEAR TONE.

WHAT'S THAT SOUND?

38

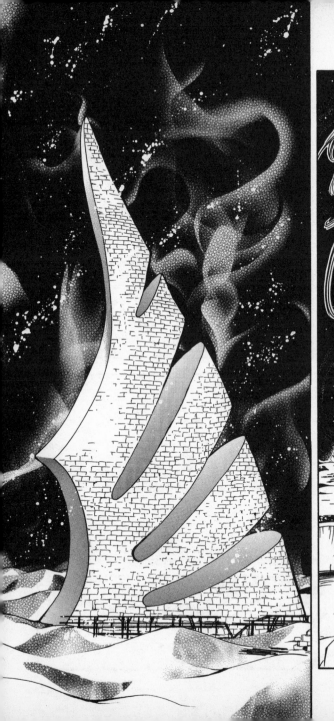

I BROUGHT LUNCH FOR US! I ASKED SOMEBODY OUTSIDE, AND HE SAID THAT YOU WERE HERE!

WHAT IS IT?

SYAORAN!

HERE!

DON'T WORRY !

TÔYA'S HERE TOO! HE'S ON AN INSPECTION OF THE SITE.

AND THE KING WILL BE WORRIED ABOUT YOU!

THERE ARE NO REINFORCE-MENTS OR SAFETY MEASURES. THE CEILING COULD FALL AT ANY TIME!

IT'S DANGER-OUS HERE!

AND THAT WHICH POINTS THE WAY ARE THE WINGS...

...THE "TSUBASA"!

THE POWER TO PASS THROUGH SPACE AND TIME.

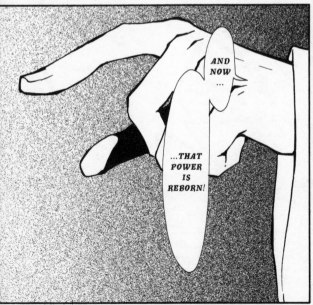

AND NOW...

...THAT POWER IS REBORN!

54

GASP

THE PRINCESS!!

THERE WAS A STRANGE RELIEF BELOW IN THE RUINS...

I WILL *NEVER* ALLOW HIM TO DIE!

SST

THE PRINCESS'S WINGS HAVE TAKEN FLIGHT.

WHAT?

I'VE READ YOUR MEMORY.

THE WINGS AND THE PRINCESS'S HEART ARE ONE.

ZZZT

HER... HEART?

ALL OF THE PRINCESS'S MEMORIES FROM THE MOMENT OF HER BIRTH TO NOW HAVE VANISHED.

...HER HEART IS NOWHERE TO BE FOUND ON THIS WORLD!

AND...

HOW CAN THAT—

60

SAKURA!!

64

RESERVoir CHRoNiCLE

Chapitre.2
The Price of Memory

70

LOOK, I WANT TO BE BETTER THAN I AM!

I WANT TO BE THE BEST!!

AND IF MY ENEMY LIVES OR DIES IN THE PROCESS, IT'S NOT MY WORRY!

THAT'S WHY I FIGHT!

THERE ARE NONE IN THE COUNTRY OF JAPAN WHO ARE STRONGER THAN YOU.

TRUE.

WHAT'S GOING ON?

EH?

SO...WE HAVE NO CHOICE LEFT.

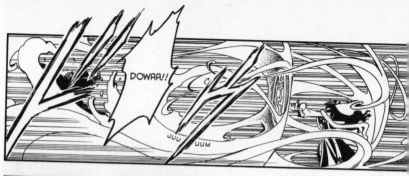

IN THE OLD DAYS, THEY ALWAYS SAID THAT THE BAD ONES MUST JOURNEY TO GET BETTER.

THEY NEVER SAID THAT!!

I DON'T WANT TO FLY!!

SO NOW I'LL SEND YOU FLYING TO ANOTHER WORLD.

72

IT IS THERE THAT YOU WILL LEARN THE TRUE MEANING OF STRENGTH.

YOU WILL MEET A GREAT MANY NEW PEOPLE.

AH, I NEARLY FORGOT.

YOU REQUIRE ONE LAST USE OF MY ARTS.

ALTHOUGH IT PAINS ME GREATLY, I WILL SEE YOU OFF.

AND TO THAT END...

WHAT THE HELL IS *THIS!*

YOU'RE NOT SEEING ME OFF, YOU'RE *FORCING* ME OFF!

TSK TSK

HO HO HO HO

FARE-WELL.

AND IF FATE ALLOWS IT, WE'LL MEET AGAIN.

HOW DARE YOU ADDRESS HER HIGH-NESS THAT WAY?

CUT THIS OUT, TOMOYO!

PLEASE BE WELL ON YOUR JOURNEY...

...KURO-GANE!

ZUBOK

ZUBOK

I'LL BE BACK, AND DON'T YOU FORGET IT!!

ZU BOPH

A CURSE.

FROM THIS MOMENT ON, UNNECESSARY DEATH WILL BE FORBIDDEN TO YOU.

FOR EACH PERSON YOU KILL, YOUR STRENGTH WILL LESSEN. I SUGGEST YOU TAKE CARE.

The Country of
SERESU

78

I STILL DON'T UNDERSTAND.

MAYBE...

...NOT EVEN THIS WORLD...

...HUH?

MMMM.

GOO CHI

GOO CHI

FOR *YOU*, CHI... ...THAT'S ALL RIGHT.

I MEAN THIS DIMENSION.

WORLD?

WHOOPS. I'M ALMOST OUT OF TIME.

I HAVE TO BE ON MY WAY.

TO WHERE?

CHI?

WHOOM

SO I WONDER IF IT'S ALL RIGHT TO CHANGE YOU A LITTLE.

IT'S JUST FINE.

I WANT YOU TO TELL ME IF THE KING AWAKENS.

BUT I HAVE A FAVOR TO ASK OF YOU, CHI.

WHAT IS IT?

PAAA AAA

AFTER ALL, FAI *MADE* CHI!

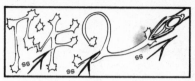

ALL RIGHT!

FWOOON

...TO SEE THE WITCH!

TIME TO GO...

GLOOB

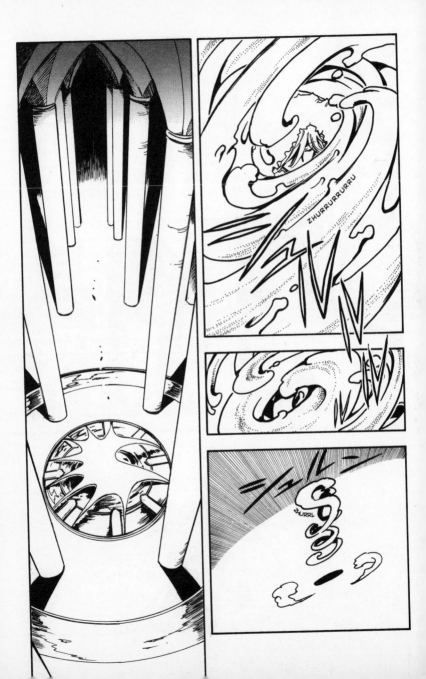

YES!

THIS CHILD'S NAME IS SAKURA, ISN'T IT?

I'M SYAORAN.

AND YOU?

THIS CHILD...

...HAS LOST SOMETHING VERY PRECIOUS.

...YES.

YOU WISH TO SAVE THIS CHILD?

YES!!

UM... ER...

AH!

TMP TMP TMP TMP

WATANUKI?

Y- YES?

GO TO OUR TREASURE ROOM, THERE IS SOMETHING I NEED YOU TO BRING BACK.

THERE IS A PRICE.

ARE YOU STILL WILLING?

KEEEEEEE

GASP

I WILL PAY ANY PRICE I CAN!

89

EH HEH.

WHO THE HELL ARE YOU?

ARE YOU THE DIMENSION WITCH?

WHAAA? はははは。

GRR

I MEAN...

...WHAT *IS* THIS PLACE?

WHAT ARE THESE WEIRD BUILDINGS ALL AROUND?

ME? I'M KUROGANE.

IT'S CALLED JAPAN.

PLEASE GIVE ME YOUR NAMES FIRST.

AND YOU?

I'M NOT GETTING ANY OF THIS!

NOT ONE BIT!

YES. A DIFFERENT JAPAN.

MY COUNTRY'S CALLED JAPAN, TOO.

EH?

THE WIZARD OF SERESU.

FAI D. FLOWRIGHT.

DO YOU KNOW WHERE YOU ARE?

YES...

AND SO...

...THE REASON WHY ALL OF YOU ARE HERE...

...IS BECAUSE EACH OF YOU HAS A WISH.

THAT'S EXACTLY IT.

A PLACE WHERE ANY WISH CAN BE GRANTED IF A SUITABLE PRICE IS PAID.

93

STARE

...FOR BOTH OF YOU.

THAT IS A TALL ORDER...

NO...

MY HOME WORLD...

...IS THE PLACE I DO *NOT* WANT TO BE.

...IS WHERE I WANT TO BE!

...FOR ALL *THREE* OF YOU...

...PERHAPS.

94

WHAT KIND OF *CRAP* ARE YOU SPOUTING?

MR. BLACK, CAN YOU KEEP YOUR INSULTS DOWN?

HEY!

I'M NOT "MR. BLACK!"

I'M KUROGANE!!

...BUT...

...IF ALL THREE PAID TOGETHER, YOU MAY JUST BE ABLE TO AFFORD IT.

EVEN IF YOU OFFERED THE MOST PRECIOUS THINGS YOU OWN, NONE OF YOU HAS ENOUGH TO PAY...

ALL THREE OF YOUR WISHES ARE THE SAME.

YOU WANT TO GO TO DIFFERENT WORLDS TO AVOID RETURNING TO YOUR OWN.

YOU WANT TO RETURN TO YOUR OWN WORLD.

YOU WANT TO GO TO MANY WORLDS IN ORDER TO RESTORE THE MEMORY OF THIS CHILD.

97

HUH
?

POLEE
?

TIIVII
?

ZMM

INSTEAD YOU WILL WANDER THIS WORLD LOOKING LIKE A COSTUME-CONTEST LOSER, AND GET PICKED UP BY THE POLICE FOR CARRYING AN UNLAWFUL SWORD, AND GET PLASTERED ALL OVER THE TV FOR BEING A FREAK! IS THAT WHAT YOU WANT?

FINE!

ZMM

TWIK

THAT'S GOT TO BE A LIE!!

IT'S ALL TRUE.

YOU REALIZE THAT YOU ARE TRAPPED HERE, AND I AM THE ONLY PERSON IN THE WORLD WHO CAN GET YOU OUT?

EH HEH HEH

YOU'RE KIDDING!

WHAT WILL YOU DO?

WHEN I AM FREE FROM THIS *CURSE*, I AM COMING BACK FOR IT!

DAMMIT!!

YOUR PRICE...

...IS YOUR MARKING.

I TOLD YOU, THE PRICE IS THE THING YOU VALUE MOST.

I DON'T SUPPOSE THIS STAFF WOULD DO INSTEAD?

IT WON'T.

I GUESS I HAVE NO CHOICE.

WHAT ABOUT YOU?

NOW IS THE TIME TO HAND OVER YOUR ITEM OF HIGHEST VALUE.

AND YOU WILL BE ABLE TO TRAVEL THE WORLDS.

FINE!

YOU REALIZE THAT I HAVEN'T NAMED THE PRICE YET.

YES!

FINDING THE CHILD'S MEMORIES IS SOMETHING *YOU* WILL HAVE TO DO.

THE ONLY THING I CAN DO IS SEND YOU TO OTHER WORLDS.

THE NAME OF THIS YOUNG ONE IS MOKONA MODOKI.

MOKONA WILL LEAD YOU THROUGH THE WORLDS.

FOR THAT REASON, ONLY FATE WILL DECIDE WHEN YOUR WISHES WILL BE GRANTED.

MOKONA WILL TAKE YOU TO DIFFERENT DIMENSIONS, BUT THERE IS NO WAY TO CONTROL WHICH DIMENSION.

NO. THAT'S HOW WE KEEP IN CONTACT.

SEE HOW USE-FUL?

TSK!

THE ONLY POWER THIS ONE HAS IS TO STAY IN COMMUNICA-TION WITH MOKONA.

HEY, YOU GOT AN EXTRA. GIVE IT TO ME.

I'LL GO HOME WITH THAT.

WHAT *IS* THERE IS "HITSUZEN."

HOWEVER, THERE IS NO COINCIDENCE IN THE WORLD.

AND WHAT BROUGHT YOU TOGETHER...

...WAS ALSO "HITSUZEN."

SYAORAN...

...YOUR PRICE IS...

...YOUR RELATION- SHIP.

106

Chapitre.3
The Wings of Hitsuzen

114

GRMP

MOKONA DRIED TOO!

WE TRIED TO DRY HER OFF.

SHE GOT PRETTY WET IN THE RAIN.

SEEP SEEP

PRAISE ME!

SO YOU...

EVEN WHILE YOU SLEPT, YOU WOULDN'T LET THE GIRL GO.

CALL ME SYAORAN.

ER...

AND... ...MR. BLACK OVER THERE. WHAT'LL WE CALL YOU?

I AM *NOT* "MR. BLACK!"

MY NAME IS PRETTY LONG.

YOU CAN JUST CALL ME FAI.

I AM KUROGANE!

YOU... THING! DON'T GET COMFORTABLE THERE!

HEY!

SO WHAT WORKS? KURO-CHAN? KURORIN?

GOT IT.

KUROGANE, HUH?

...IS LIKE *ICE!*

HER BODY...

...WE HAVE TO HELP SAKURA!

BEFORE WE START LOOKING FOR HER MEMORIES...

SHE CAN'T STAY THIS WAY!

HMMMM.

RUSTLE RUSTLE

ZWOOP

WAA!!

WHAT DO YOU THINK YOU'RE DOING?!

SHF

SHF

SII IP

...FOR THIS CHILD?

IS THIS WHAT A PIECE OF MEMORY LOOKS LIKE...

ONLY ONE, THOUGH.

IT WAS STUCK TO YOU.

EH?!

AND SO...

...MY GUESS IS WITHOUT THINKING, YOU GRABBED IT YOURSELF.

THAT'S...

...WHAT THE WITCH SAID, WASN'T IT?

BYUUN

IN ORDER TO SAVE THE GIRL.

BUT MY QUESTION IS HOW CAN WE FIND THEM NOW...

I DOUBT WE'LL FIND ANY MORE IN OUR CLOTHES.

MUDGE MUDGE

...NEW FEATHERS.

OF COURSE, I'M JUST GUESSING ALL THIS!

......

GYUNS

SLUMP

EHP

HUH?

THAT FEATHER GAVE OUT *REALLY* BIG WAVES!

MEEEEE! MEE! ME!

SO WHEN A FEATHER IS CLOSE, MOKONA WILL FEEL THE BIG WAVES!

MOKONA KNOWS!!

AND MOKONA WILL BE LIKE...

GAK!

BWAHH

...THIS!!

DON'T EXPECT ME TO STICK MY NECK OUT FOR YOU. DON'T EXPECT ME TO HELP YOU.

I WON'T DO IT!

I'M HERE TO GET BACK TO MY OWN WORLD.

THAT'S THE ONLY REASON I'M HERE.

HA HA HA HA HA! SYAORAN, YOU ARE SO *SERIOUS*!

I'LL DO MY BEST NOT TO CAUSE YOU ANY TROUBLE.

RIGHT.

THAT IS *MY* MISSION HERE.

NOD

TSKI

?

I'M SORATA ARISUGAWA.

HERE.

OH! THANK YOU!

JUST TO LET YOU KNOW, SHE'S MY WIFE AND THE WOMAN I LOVE.

I CALL HER MY "HONEY"!

NOT LISTENING

無視

ヒュー

HEFT

JUST MAKE SURE YOU'VE BURNED THAT INTO YOUR HEARTS.

BOW

I'M ARASHI.

BY WHICH I MEAN THAT IF YOU LAY A FINGER ON HER, YOU'LL DIE HORRIBLY. ♡

POFF

TWRL

WHAT BLISS I FEEL HAVING A HONEY LIKE THIS!

I'M SYRO-RAN.

HERE.

AHH...

BOW

NORI! NORI!

NORI IS LIFE!

AH HA HA HA

WHY DO YOU SAY THAT ONLY TO ME?!

I WON'T TOUCH HER!!

BRIGHT SMILEY FACE

HUP

BUT I WASN'T KIDDING!

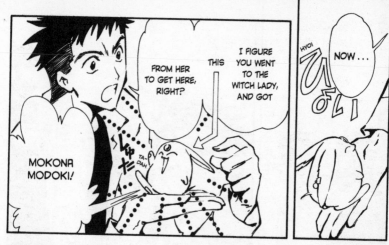

NOW . . .

HYO!

FROM HER TO GET HERE, RIGHT?

THIS

I FIGURE YOU WENT TO THE WITCH LADY, AND GOT

MOKONA MODOKI!

TA-DAH!

SURE!

OKAY!

IS IT OKAY IF I JUST SAY MOKONA?

THAT'S A LONG NAME.

I MEAN THE BLONDE GUY.

MR. BLACK OVER THERE IS TOO MEAN TO ASK!

SHUT UP!

EH HEH.

I HEARD THE WHOLE STORY FROM THE MAN THERE.

ANYWAY, GENTLE-MEN . . .

UMM . . .

THIS IS YOUR LUCKY DAY.

SO . . .

. . . IT'S A HAPPY CHANCE THAT BROUGHT YOU TO THIS WORLD FIRST OF ALL.

MOKONA HAS NO IDEA WHICH IS THE NEXT WORLD, RIGHT?

IN WHAT WAY?

BECAUSE THIS . . .

RESERVoir CHRoNiCLE

Chapitre.4
The Strength to Fight

THIS IS THE HANSHIN REPUBLIC.

THE BEST OF ISLAND NATIONS.

WE ARE SURROUNDED BY SEAS ON ALL SIDES. WE GET THE ODD HURRICANE, BUT WE HARDLY EVER HAVE EARTHQUAKES...

WE HAVE SEVERAL TRADING PARTNERS ACROSS THE SEAS, AND WE EXPORT LIKE CRAZY!

TIGER SAUCE

AND OUR SAUCE IS FAMOUS!

THE MAIN STAPLE IS WHEAT FLOUR.

THE SEASON WHERE RICE TASTES ITS BEST!

RIGHT NOW, WE'RE IN FALL.

WE HAVE FOUR SEASONS.

春 SPRING GREAT FLOWER VIEWING!

夏 SUMMER SEASON FOR BEER!

秋 FALL RICE TASTES ITS BEST!

冬 WINTER BEST SEASON FOR NABE!

AND BY LAW, WE NEVER MAKE WAR WITH OTHER COUNTRIES.

WE HAVE THE HANSHIN REPUBLIC CONSTITUTION AND RULE OF LAW!

.....

...AND ONE COULD CONSIDER A *BABY CARRIAGE* TO BE ONE FORM OF TRANSPORT, RIGHT HONEY?

PLANE ...

BOAT ...

TRAIN ...

MOTOR-CYCLE ...

BICYCLE ...

CAR ...

MODES OF TRANS-PORT...

THE SHAPE OF THE ISLAND IS THUS.

BECAUSE OF THE SIMILARITY TO A TIGER, PEOPLE CALL US THE TIGER COUNTRY.

OF COURSE, THE HANSHIN REPUBLIC USES THE IMAGE OF A TIGER QUITE A BIT.

OUR CURRENCY IS THE KOKO. (TIGER)

THERE ARE ONE-KOKO COINS, 100,000 KOKO BILLS, AND THE TIGER HEAD IS THE SYMBOL OF THE COUNTRY.

AND THE LOGO FOR OUR BASEBALL TEAM IS THE SAME!

.....

I HAVE A QUESTION!

SIR!

BUT THE TEAM'S A ROUGH & TUMBLE GROUP OUTSIDE THE PARK!

SOME OF THE BEST PLAYERS IN THE WORLD!

THIS YEAR, THE TEAM HAS SOME REALLY GREAT PROSPECTS!

DOES EVERYONE IN THIS COUNTRY HAVE AN ACCENT LIKE YOURS, SORATA-SAN?

BASEBALL? WHAT THE HELL IS THAT?

YES?

FAI-KUN?

YOURS IS A LANGUAGE THAT THEY USED IN THE PAST?

MY ACCENT IS UNIQUE TO ME. IT'S AN OLDER VERSION OF OUR LANGUAGE.

AWW, DON'T BE SO FORMAL! CALL ME SORA-CHAN!

OMAAAA!

OMAAA!

SORA-CHAN?

YOU'RE A HISTORY TEACHER?

I'M A HISTORY TEACHER, AND I'M FIRMLY AGAINST ALLOWING ALL THE OLD WAYS TO FADE AWAY.

THAT'S RIGHT!

NOWADAYS HARDLY ANYONE USES THIS LANGUAGE.

BOING

AND I HAVE ONE MORE QUESTION!

MEEE!

MEEE!

はーい

はーい

はーい

THEN I'D SAY WE HAVE SOMETHING IN COMMON!

IN MY WORLD, I USED TO WORK ON ARCHAEO-LOGICAL DIGS.

YES!

I TAKE IT YOU HAVE AN INTEREST IN HISTORY?

I AM!

あうっ!!

GOOD QUESTION!

NOW ...

EXACTLY WHERE ARE WE? WHO OWNS THIS ROOM?

AIN'T IT GREAT?

A BEAUTIFUL APARTMENT MANAGER WHO IS ALSO A GREAT COOK!

THIS IS AN EMPTY ROOM IN AN OLD, TRADITIONAL APARTMENT HOUSE THAT MY HONEY AND I MANAGE.

GAMPH

WAY OUT OF IT

うっとり・・・

・・・・・

143

144

I DIDN'T FEEL AN ENEMY! WHO DID THAT?

BASTARD! *YOU* THREW THAT, DIDN'T YOU?

IT HAD TO COME FROM ABOVE.

YOU WERE IN A CORNER. IF HE THREW ANYTHING, IT WOULDN'T HIT YOU THERE.

WHAT?

IT WAS MY *KUDAN*, WHAT ELSE?

"KUDAN"?

YOU ALL COME FROM DIFFERENT WORLDS! YOU WOULDN'T KNOW!

SURE YOU DON'T!

YOU DON'T KNOW?

HERE'S HOW IT'S WRITTEN IN KANJI.

巧断

SQUEEK

EVERYONE IN THIS WORLD HAS A KUDAN ATTACHED.

HEE HEE HEE

THAT'S REALLY GREAT, MOKONA!

AH...

I SEE.

I DON'T SEE AT ALL!

BUT YOU CAN UNDERSTAND WHAT I SAY, AND I UNDERSTAND YOU.

KUROGANE AND SYAORAN'S WORLDS USE KANJI, BUT FAI'S PROBABLY DOESN'T.

CAN YOU, SYAORAN?

YEAH.

MORE OR LESS.

AH HA HA HA HA HA HA

HMM. HMM.

POK

巧断

MOKONA CAN READ!!

I NEVER HAD MAGIC OR WEAPONS OR ANYTHING LIKE THAT FROM THE START.

IT WASN'T ANY SORT OF POWER THAT I GAVE HER.

EH?

THAT MAY HAVE BEEN YOUR GOOD LUCK.

THEN THIS KUDAN WAS ORIGINALLY MEANT FOR BATTLE?

THERE ARE KUDAN IN THIS WORLD.

WHEN IT COMES TIME TO FIGHT, THAT KUDAN SHOULD BE ABLE TO HELP.

YES!

SHALL WE FIND...

...THIS FEATHER OF YOURS?

AND YOU MEN, DO YOU FEEL THE SAME?

MOKONA...

...WILL NOT LEAVE THIS COUNTRY UNTIL MOKONA FINDS THE FEATHER!

NO!

I MIGHT AS WELL.

WHITE THING?

IF I SAID I WANTED TO LEAVE, WOULD YOU DO IT...

THANK
YOU...

...MOKONA
!

WHILE
YOU'RE ON
THIS WORLD,
I'LL VOUCH
FOR YOU.

FINE.

YOU CAN
USE THESE
ROOMS
UNTIL YOU
GO TO
YOUR NEXT
WORLD.

THIS IS AN
APARTMENT
BUILDING.
WE'VE GOT
ROOM.

THANK
YOU VERY
MUCH!

SEE...

I OWE
YÛKO-SAN
A FAVOR.

IT'S AFTER MIDNIGHT ALREADY.

I'LL SHOW YOU TO YOUR ROOMS.

IT'S TIME TO SLEEP.

YOU CAN USE THIS ROOM.

THANK YOU VERY MUCH.

RATTL RATTL

I'M NOT A STRANGER! I TOLD YOU MY NAME, DIDN'T I?

WHY DO I HAVE TO STAY WITH A COMPLETE STRANGER!

WHAT WAS THAT?!

NOT AT ALL!

FAI AND KUROGANE, YOU DON'T MIND SHARING, DO YOU?

RATTL

RATTL

AND SAKURA-SAN . . .

YOU'RE STRANGER THAN ALL THE REST!

MOKONA TOLD YOU MOKONA'S NAME!

I...

...WANT TO STAY BY HER SIDE.

YOU'LL BE PROTECTED BY MY HONEY AND MYSELF.

BOING

RELAX AND SLEEP TONIGHT.

モコナ小狼と寝る

MOKONA WILL SLEEP WITH SYAORAN!

VERY WELL.

BUT YOU MUST GET AT LEAST SOME SLEEP FOR YOURSELF.

YOU HAVE NO IDEA WHAT AWAITS YOU OR WHAT WILL HAPPEN IN THIS COUNTRY.

WHEN THERE IS A CHANCE TO SLEEP, YOU SHOULD SLEEP.

ALL RIGHT.

パタ—ン

KACHAK

BYE BYE!

ばいばい

Chapitre.5
The Instant of Awakening

MOKONA ISN'T A WHITE THING! MOKONA IS MOKONA!

BAA

STAY AWAY!

IS THE WHITE THING COMING ALONG, TOO?

I'LL STAY BY SAKURA-SAN'S SIDE FOR YOU.

DUCK

THANK YOU.

HUH?

WHAT I MEAN IS THIS WORLD IS USED TO WEIRD SIGHTS.

GRRRR

RIGHT!

IF MOKONA IS A WHITE THING, THEN THIS GUY HERE IS A BLACK THING, RIGHT?

YOU HAVE TO TAKE MOKONA, OR YOU'LL PASS THE FEATHER BY AND NEVER KNOW!

DON'T WORRY. NOBODY WILL GIVE MOKONA A SECOND THOUGHT.

WELL, YOU CAN EAT WHERE YOU LIKE, BUT YOU'LL NEVER FIND A BETTER MEAL THAN MY HONEY MAKES!

THERE'S ENOUGH FOR LUNCH IN THERE, SO THE THREE OF YOU SHOULD TAKE YOUR TIME AND MAKE FRIENDS.

NOW...

WHY'S HE GIVING IT TO THE *KID*?!

TAKE THIS.

WHAT'S *THAT* SUPPOSED TO MEAN?

GLINT

AH HA HA HA HA HA

GLINT

YUP!

NOD

CAUSE HE'S THE ONE WHO LOOKS THE MOST TRUSTWORTHY!

BLAH BLAH

BLAH

166

IT SURE IS A BUSTLING PLACE!

PEOPLE ALL OVER THE PLACE!

EVERY-THING'S WEIRD HERE!

SMALL BUILDINGS ARE BUNCHED UP NEXT TO THE HUGE ONES!

AND WHY DO YOU HAVE TO CALL ME BY WEIRDER AND WEIRDER NAMES?!

NEVER!

KURO-TAN, HOW ABOUT YOU?

GRR

TWRL

SYAORAN-KUN, HAVE YOU EVER SEEN THIS KIND OF THING?

NO. NEVER.

HUP UP UP

THE SHAPE IS THE SAME, BUT IN MY WORLD, THE COLOR IS A PALE YELLOW.

HMP?

SO IT DIDN'T LOOK LIKE THAT ON YOUR WORLD?

ZUU UIP

WAAA!

MAKE UP YOUR MIND!

OOP!

AND...

...DO YOU WANT IT OR *NOT?!*

ISN'T THAT CALLED A PEAR?

NO.

NO, THAT'S A RAKI SEED, ISN'T IT?

A PEAR IS REDDER AND HAS LEAVES COMING OUT OF THE TOP.

WANT IT!!

HUH?

NICE DOIN' BUSINESS WITH YA.

169

...IT REALLY IS TRUE THAT THE THREE OF US COME FROM COMPLETELY DIFFERENT CULTURES.

BUT...

WHAT IS THIS TASTE?

YES.

THESE APPLES ARE PRETTY GOOD, HUH?

CHOMP

THAT'S IMPRESSIVE. IT'S HARD ENOUGH TO SEND ONE PERSON ACROSS DIMENSIONS. BUT HE SENT TWO.

THERE'S A HIGH PRIEST IN MY LAND. HE SENT ME.

AHHH!

COME TO THINK OF IT, I NEVER ASKED... HOW DID YOU GET TO THE SHOP OF THE DIMENSION WITCH, SYAORAN-KUN?

YOU SAID THAT THERE WAS NO MAGIC IN YOUR WORLD, DIDN'T YOU?

BOING

I TOLD YOU TO STOP THAT!

GULP

HOW ABOUT YOU, KURO-RIN?

THE PRINCESS OF MY COUNTRY SENT ME AWAY— BY FORCE.

IT WOULD TAKE GOING TO A LOT OF WORLDS TO BE ABLE TO COLLECT ALL OF SAKURA-CHAN'S FEATHERS.

AND I THINK THE ONLY ONE WHO CAN SEND SOMEONE TO MANY WORLDS IS THE DIMENSION WITCH.

"YOUR HIGHNESS, WOULD YOU HAVE AN APPLE?"

"THANK YOU!"

173

190

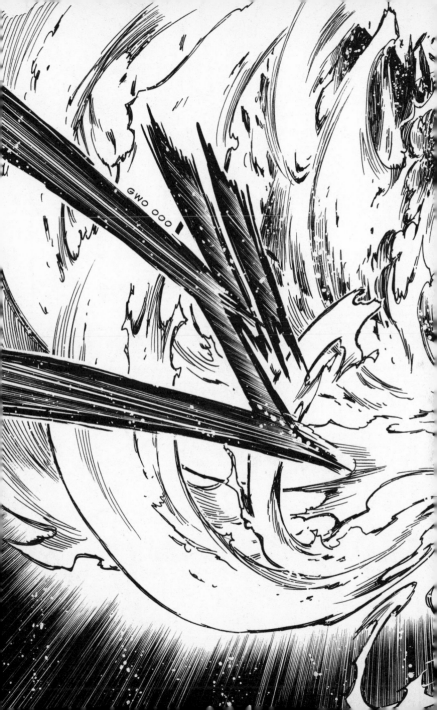

YOU SEEM TO HAVE A SPECIAL KUDAN, DON'T YOU?

To Be Continued

About the Creators

CLAMP is a group of four women who have become the most popular manga artists in America—Ageha Ohkawa, Mokona, Satsuki Igarashi, and Tsubaki Nekoi. They started out as doujnishi (fan comics) creators, but their skill and craft brought them to the attention of publishers very quickly. Their first work from a major publisher was *RG Veda*, but their first mass success was with *Magic Knight Rayearth*. From there, they went on to write many series, including *Cardcaptor Sakura* and *Chobits*, two of the most popular manga in the United States. Like many Japanese manga artists, they prefer to avoid the spotlight, and little is known about them personally.

CLAMP is currently publishing three series in Japan: *Tsubasa* and *xxxHOLiC* with Kodansha and *Gohou Drug* with Kadokawa.

Past Works

CLAMP has created many series. Here is a brief overview of one of them.

Cardcaptor Sakura

The first volume of *Cardcaptor Sakura* was released in Japan in 1996, and by the time the series was finished it would number twelve volumes in all. The first six, called simply *Cardcaptor Sakura*, are the story of fourth-grader Sakura, who finds a magic book called *The Clow* in her father's library. The book and its magical guardian, Kero, were responsible for containing the Clow Cards. The Clow Cards, created by sorcerer Clow Reed, have escaped, and Kero needs Sakura's help to find them. Empowered with the key to recapture them, Sakura becomes a Cardcaptor and begins her quest for all of the lost Clow cards.

Over the course of the next six volumes, we are introduced to a wide range of characters, some of whom will be familiar to you after you've read the first volume of *Tsubasa*. Toya is Sakura's brother, and Yukito is his best friend. Li Syaoran is Sakura's erstwhile competitor in capturing the Clow Cards. Still, there are more characters that don't appear in *Tsubasa* than do, such as Kero, the guardian.

If you've read *Cardcaptor Sakura*, even the characters you recognize will seem radically different. The *Tsubasa* versions of Sakura and Syaoran both seem to be teenagers, several years older than their counterparts. Toya is a king, while Yuki is his chief advisor. Toya and Sakura's parents aren't in the picture, while Tomoyo lives in yet another dimension and appears to have no knowledge of Sakura whatsoever!

Cardcaptor Sakura was released in anime form in two versions in the United States. Pioneer released the Japanese version on DVD, while Nelvana released a reworked version on television called simply *Cardcaptors*. *Cardcaptors* was short-lived and incurred the ire of many fans because it was heavily edited and reworked to make it more palatable for an American audience.

In the manga, the main storyline ends in volume six when Sakura successfully captures all of the Clow Cards and is named Master of the Clow. It almost looks like it's time for Sakura to hang up her wand for good, but CLAMP still had a few more stories in mind—and another six volumes to go!

189

Dramatis Personae

You'd need a scorecard to keep track of all the characters who will be appearing in *Tsubasa* and *xxxHOLiC*, so we've decided to create one for you. Some of these characters will look familiar, but you haven't really met most of them before. Don't read these if you haven't read this volume yet—there's a reason we put them at the end of the book!

Sakura

While it's clear that Sakura is older than her counterpart from *Cardcaptor Sakura*, we don't actually know her age yet. She is the princess of Clow, raised by her brother, King Toya. She's a happy princess, well-loved by her people. Sakura possesses the power to change the world, but it will be a while before she—or we—understand what that means.

Syaoran

Syaoran's father died in an archaeological dig, leaving him an orphan, but Syaoran felt compelled to continue his father's work. He's closer than ever to uncovering the secrets of the giant wings buried in the sand, but a threat to Sakura's safety sends him on a quest to save her life! The *Tsubasa* version of Syaoran is very different from the character in *Cardcaptor Sakura*. Where the CS Syaoran is dour, surly, even rude at times, *Tsubasa*'s version is open, friendly—and clearly in love with Sakura.

Tomoyo

In *CS*, Tomoyo was Sakura's best friend who videotaped her card-capturing exploits. In *Tsubasa*, Tomoyo is the queen of another realm, and like Yukito, she is a powerful sorceress. It remains to be seen if her role in this drama is concluded.

Fai D. Florite

Fai's motivation for visiting Yûko, the space-time witch, isn't entirely clear. Like Tomoyo, he is the ruler of his land of Seresu. He may be fleeing a battle he's lost, or he may desperately need to get away from a battle he's won—we just don't know yet. What we do know is that he is the creator of this world's version of Chi, a character from CLAMP's *Chobits*, and that he is fleeing from Ashura, a variation of the main character of CLAMP's first series, *RG Veda*.

Chi

In *Chobits*, Chi was a persocom, a personal computer found by Hideki Motosuwa. With her memory wiped clean, Chi and Hideki have a lot of work to do to discover her origins. Along the way, each discovers a lot more about themselves and about their feelings for each other. Of course, that's assuming that a machine can even have feelings in the first place. . . .

The *Tsubasa* version of Chi was created by Fai, so she is clearly *not* the same character as in *Chobits*, although her personality appears remarkably similar. As Fai begins his quest, he leaves Chi behind to guard against King Ashura's awakening.

Yûko

Yûko is a witch. She lives in a
peculiar house in Tokyo with two
peculiar helpers, Maru and Moru.
Her work is simple: She helps
people . . . for a price. The price is
never more than her customer can
bear, but the greater the need, the

higher it gets. Yûko is something of an enigma: She comes across as
very mysterious and all-knowing, but she also has a playful,
sometimes wild side that leads to unfortunate side effects. Like
hangovers.

Watanuki

Watanuki Kimihiro will pop up in *Tsubasa* from time
to time, but his home is over in *xxxHOLiC*, where he
works for Yûko, cleaning, cooking, gardening, and
doing whatever other chores Yûko can come up with.
It's the price he pays for Yûko to grant his wish—to be
rid of the spirit visions that haunt him. Although he's a
hard worker, he often finds working for Yûko to be a
frustrating experience.

Sorata (Sora) Arisugawa

When Sora was three years old, the Buddhist monks of Mt. Koya recognized Sora as a future Dragon of Heaven. Knowing that he would develop powers that could help to save the earth, the monks started training him, and Sora's irrepressible personality turned the monastery upside down. But when the three-year-old Sora was parted from his mother, the tears in her eyes affected him deeply. He determined that he would find the one girl for him, and he would protect her. He would protect her and die for her so that she may never feel hurt the way his mother did. In the story of X (*X/1999*), the girl he found was Arashi Kishu.

Arashi Kishu

At age six, Arashi was wandering the streets eating out of garbage cans and wondering if life was really worth it. Her mother had died three months earlier, and although she had asked Arashi to somehow survive, Arashi was beginning to have second thoughts. Being found by her mother's old Shinto teacher and brought into a beautiful shrine still didn't answer Arashi's question of whether to die or go on living. The promise of becoming a Dragon of Heaven, and more importantly, having friends in the future so that she wouldn't be alone, made Arashi decide to give life a try. In the story of X (*X/1999*), she grew into a Shinto "miko" priestess and joined the Seven Seals.

Translation Notes

Japanese is a tricky language for most westerners, and translation is often more art than science. For your edification and reading pleasure, here are notes on some of the places where we could have gone in a different direction in our translation of the work, or where a Japanese cultural reference is used.

The Kingdom of Clow

Made up of the characters Eternal and Tower, the pronunciation *kurô* sounds suspiciously like Clow.

Intimacy

After Sakura and Syaoran's conversation, you should notice a distinct similarity between that conversation and the later one of Tôya and Yukito.

It's all about intimacy. Once two people are close enough friends, they drop the honorifics and titles (see *Honorifics* at the front of the book) and the grammar of polite language, and they become more direct and easygoing.

195

Ginryû

The characters for Ginryû mean "silver dragon," which gives you the reason for the dragon on the hilt.

Hitsuzen

This is actually defined by Yûko in *xxxHOLiC* Volume 1: "Hitsuzen. A naturally foreordained event. A state in which other outcomes are impossible. A result which can only be obtained by a single causality, and other causalities would necessarily create different results."

Kuro-chan, Kuro-rin . . .

All of the names that Fai is trying to give Kurogane are the type of nicknames that one would give cute high-school girls (ko-gals), or that cute high-school girls would give themselves.

Sora's Accent

Accents in Japanese and English work somewhat differently. In English, an accent is mostly marked by pronunciation—especially of the vowel sounds—and a few differences in vocabulary. So if you take a little time to get used to the differences, you will have no problem understanding even the thickest accent in English. In Japanese, there are some pronunciation differences, but most of the differences are in vocabulary. Since the differences start at the core vocabulary (even the ubiquitous verb "to be"!), and spread throughout, a thick accent is nearly as difficult to understand as a completely different language. Fortunately for most Japanese citizens, the Osaka dialect is very popular in the media, so everyone is used to the different words, even if they didn't grow up in the Osaka area.

The Hanshin Republic

For those who don't know Japanese baseball, the most popular team in Japan is the Yomiuri Giants. The second most popular team is the Hanshin Tigers, and like other second-mosts, the fans of the Hanshin Tigers are fiercely competitive and fanatical. None more than Sora's character, and so, the Hanshin Republic is the fondest dream of Tigers' fans—an

The logo for the Hanshin Tigers

entire nation devoted body and soul to Osaka's favorite baseball club. More on this in Volume 2!

Preview of *Tsubasa* Volume 2

Here is an excerpt from Volume 2, on sale now in English.

俺は浅黄笙悟だ

おまえは？

・・・・小狼

おまえ気にいった

CLAMP

TRANSLATED AND ADAPTED BY
Anthony Gerard

LETTERED BY
Dana Hayward

Tsubasa crosses over with *xxxHOLiC*. Although it isn't necessary to read *xxxHOLiC* to understand the events in *Tsubasa*, you'll get to see the same events from different perspectives if you read both!

Contents

Honorifics Explained

Throughout the Del Rey Manga books, you will find Japanese honorifics left intact in the translations. For those not familiar with how the Japanese use honorifics, and more important, how they differ from American honorifics, we present this brief overview.

Politeness has always been a critical facet of Japanese culture. Ever since the feudal era, when Japan was a highly stratified society, use of honorifics — which can be defined as polite speech that indicates relationship or status — has played an essential role in the Japanese language. When addressing someone in Japanese, an honorific usually takes the form of a suffix attached to one's name (example: "Asuna-san"), or as a title at the end of one's name or in place of the name itself (example: "Negi-sensei," or simply "Sensei!").

Honorifics can be expressions of respect or endearment. In the context of manga and anime, honorifics give insight into the nature of the relationship between characters. Many translations into English leave out these important honorifics, and therefore distort the "feel" of the original Japanese. Because Japanese honorifics contain nuances that English honorifics lack, it is our policy at Del Rey not to translate them. Here, instead, is a guide to some of the honorifics you may encounter in Del Rey Manga.

-san: This is the most common honorific, and is equivalent to Mr., Miss, Ms., Mrs., etc. It is the all-purpose honorific and can be used in any situation where politeness is required.

-sama: This is one level higher than "-san." It is used to confer great respect.

-dono: This comes from the word "tono," which means "lord." It is even a higher level than "-sama," and confers utmost respect.

-kun: This suffix is used at the end of boys' names to express familiarity or endearment. It is also sometimes used by men among friends, or when addressing someone younger or of a lower station.

-chan: This is used to express endearment, mostly toward girls. It is also used for little boys, pets, and even among lovers. It gives a sense of childish cuteness.

Bozu: This is an informal way to refer to a boy, similar to the English term "kid" or "squirt."

Sempai: This title suggests that the addressee is one's "senior" in a group or organization. It is most often used in a school setting, where underclassmen refer to their upperclassmen as "sempai." It can also be used in the workplace, such as when a newer employee addresses an employee who has seniority in the company.

Kohai: This is the opposite of "-sempai," and is used toward underclassmen in school or newcomers in the workplace. It connotes that the addressee is of lower station.

Sensei: Literally meaning "one who has come before," this title is used for teachers, doctors, or masters of any profession or art.

-[blank]: Usually forgotten in these lists, but perhaps the most significant difference between Japanese and English. The lack of honorific means that the speaker has permission to address the person in a very intimate way. Usually, only family, spouses, or very close friends have this kind of permission. Known as *yobisute*, it can be gratifying when someone who has earned the intimacy starts to call one by one's name without an honorific. But when that intimacy hasn't been earned, it can also be very insulting.

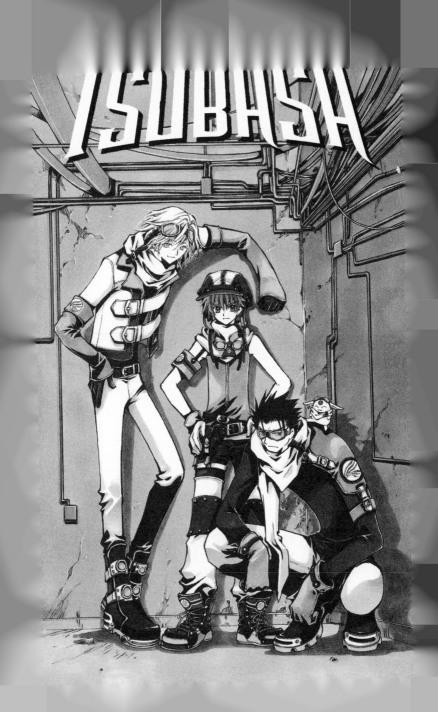

RESERVoir CHRoNiCLE

Chapitre.6
Strength of the Heart

6

AND IT WAS JUST GETTING GOOD.

SIGH

SHÔGO, THE COPS!

HOOOSH

COME ON, YA BASTARDS!

LET'S GET OUTTA HERE!

NEXT TIME WE MEET, WE'LL HAVE SOME REAL FUN!

HOOSH

HOOSH

HOOSH

HOOSH

HOLD IT!!

TMP TMP TMP

TMP

FOWOOO!!

GHOOOOO

FWOOM

!?

SHULOOM

IT... WENT... INSIDE ME.

THAT'S A "KUDAN," HUH?

I'M NOT SURE. BUT I SUDDENLY GOT VERY HOT...

THAT WAS AMAZING! SYAORAN-KUN, DID THAT COME FROM YOU?

9

IT PROBABLY GOT STEPPED ON SOMEWHERE AROUND HERE.

LIKE SOME DISCARDED PORK BUN.

AAAH!

WHAT A PAIN!

N o o o o o.

SKRITCH SKRITCH

LOOK. THE TRUTH IS QUITE DIFFERENT.

HMM?

NOW, WHERE CAN MY "ALMOST KUDAN" HAVE GOTTEN OFF TO?

GLANCE

GASP

MOKONA!!

KYAA!

KYAA!

KYAA!

KYAA!

IT'S SO CUTE!

THE SWEET-EST THING!

LOOK HOW SOFT!

MOKONA IS POPULAR WITH THE LADIES!

DID YOU FIGURE OUT WHO HAD IT?

IT WAS...

BUT MOKONA DOESN'T FEEL IT ANYMORE.

OH... I SEE.

GLOOM

SHAKE SHAKE SHAKE

DON'T KNOW.

YES!

MOKONA WILL GO ALL-OUT!

AND IF YOU SENSE ANYTHING MORE, LET US KNOW.

THUMP

STILL, WE NOW KNOW THAT SOMEONE CLOSE BY HAS IT.

THAT'S PRETTY GOOD PROGRESS.

EVEN IF WE LIMIT IT TO THE PEOPLE WHO WERE HERE, IT'LL STILL BE A LONG SEARCH.

THERE WERE LOTS OF PEOPLE.

HMM.

EH?

UMM...
UMM...

あの
あの

I ORDERED MODAN-YAKI, BUT MAYBE TONPEI-YAKI WOULD HAVE BEEN BETTER.

Y'SEE... OKONOMIYAKI IS MY FAVORITE DISH, SO...

SSSZZZZ

WHAT IS...

STARE

B-BMP   B-BMP

OKONO-MIYAKI IS A STAPLE OF THE DIET IN THE HANSHIN REPUBLIC.

IF YOU DON'T KNOW, THEN THAT MUST MEAN...

"OKONO-MIYAKI"?

IS THAT WHAT THIS IS CALLED?

AND IF BAD PEOPLE ARE AROUND, THEY TAKE CARE OF THE PROBLEM!

THEY PATROL THEIR TERRITORY MAKING SURE NO BAD KIDS CAUSE TROUBLE.

THERE ...

...THERE ARE BAD TEAMS, BUT THERE ARE GOOD TEAMS, TOO!

BUT THINK OF THE LIVES PUT IN DANGER WHEN THEY FIGHT IN SUCH A LARGE PUBLIC PLACE.

THAT'S BECAUSE I'M JUST USELESS.

♪ THIS OKONOMIYAKI LOOKS GREAT!

LIKE A LOCAL MILITIA?

WHAT ABOUT THOSE TWO TEAMS BEFORE?

STARE

THAT'S TRUE, HUH?

MASAYOSHI-KUN HERE WAS IN BIG TROUBLE.

WHEN THEY BATTLE OTHER TEAMS, SOME OF THE SURROUNDING BUILDINGS GET DAMAGED, SO THE ADULTS ARE AFRAID OF THEM ... BUT THEY WOULDN'T DO ANYTHING ELSE THAT'S BAD!

THEY'RE REALLY COOL!

BUT THE ONES IN GOGGLES AREN'T LIKE THEM AT ALL!

THE ONES IN CAPS WERE THE BAD ONES!

OH!

SMELLS GREAT!

STARE

IT'S SO BIG AND STRONG... EVERYONE WISHES THEY HAD A KUDAN JUST LIKE IT!

ESPECIALLY THEIR LEADER, SHÔGO-SAN!

THEY SAY HIS KUDAN IS SPECIAL LEVEL!

I-I SURE DO!

LOOK AT ALL THE CABBAGE!

STAAARE

I... I'M SORRY.

ZLIP ZLIP

SLUMP

STARE

BLUSH

THUMPA

THUMPA

THUMPA

AND YOU WISH YOU HAD A FRIEND JUST LIKE HIM, HUH?

STARE

EH?

BUT I'D ALSO LIKE A FRIEND LIKE SYAORAN-KUN!

...IS JUST AMAZING!

ANYBODY WITH A SPECIAL LEVEL KUDAN...

SO, WHAT IS THAT? SPECIAL LEVEL?

HMM.

DIDN'T THE LEADER OF THAT GOGGLE TEAM SAY SOMETHING ABOUT A SPECIAL KUDAN...?

STARE

IT'S AN ESPECIALLY HIGH LEVEL FOR KUDAN.

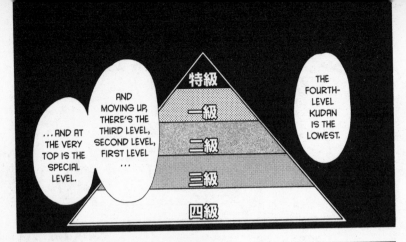

特級

一級

二級

三級

四級

...AND AT THE VERY TOP IS THE SPECIAL LEVEL.

AND MOVING UP, THERE'S THE THIRD LEVEL, SECOND LEVEL, FIRST LEVEL...

THE FOURTH-LEVEL KUDAN IS THE LOWEST.

THEN...

...THAT LEADER'S KUDAN MUST BE VERY STRONG.

...BUT NORMAL PEOPLE STILL USE THE SYSTEM.

YEARS AGO, ALL THE COUNTRIES GOT TOGETHER AND BANNED THE USE OF LEVELS ON KUDAN...

YEAH!

TWITCH

SO IS SYAORAN-KUN'S!

IT'S A PERSON'S HEART THAT CONTROLS A KUDAN.

SO IF A PERSON CAN COMMAND A STRONG KUDAN, THAT'S PROOF THAT THE PERSON IS STRONG!

TO GET A STRONG KUDAN, ESPECIALLY A SPECIAL-LEVEL KUDAN, YOU NEED TO BE A STRONG PERSON YOUR-SELF, OR THEY WON'T STAY!

WHO WOULDN'T WANT A FRIEND LIKE THAT?

KUNCH

MY KUDAN ...IS FOURTH LEVEL— THE VERY BOTTOM.

MASAYOSHI-KUN ...

20

NOW THAT YOU MEN- TION IT...

BUT *WHEN* DID SYAORAN- KUN'S KUDAN JOIN UP WITH HIM?

I HAD AN ODD DREAM LAST NIGHT.

A DREAM?

STOP RIGHT THERE !!

Chapitre.7
Linked Worlds

RESERVoir CHRoNiCLE

AND THE GUY WITH HIM WAS THE HIGH PRIEST...

LEAVE IT, WILL YA?

"YOUR MAJESTY"! THAT SOUNDS COOL!

WITH OKONOMIYAKI HERE, THE WAITERS DO ALL THE COOKING FOR YOU. YOU DON'T HAVE TO DO ANYTHING.

IS THAT RIGHT...?

BUSTLE

YES...

MAJESTY... WAS HE A KING IN YOUR WORLD?

IT'S JUST LIKE THE SPACE-TIME WITCH SAID...

SHADDUP!

YOU GOT YELLED AT!

"...THEY'VE DEVELOPED UNDER COMPLETELY DIFFERENT CONDITIONS ON OTHER WORLDS."

"PEOPLE YOU'VE MET ON YOUR WORLD..."

THE TWO FROM SYAORAN'S WORLD LIVED A COMPLETELY DIFFERENT LIFE THAN THESE TWO.

EXCUSE MEP

? ? ?

THEY'RE THE SAME... AND NOT THE SAME.

YOU'RE SAYING THAT THEY'RE THE SAME AS THE KING AND HIGH PRIEST OF THE KID'S WORLD?

BUT WHEN IT COMES DOWN TO IT...

...AT THE VERY BASIC LEVEL, THEY'RE THE SAME.

I GUESS.

"SOUL"!

THAT'S WHAT YOU'RE SAYING, RIGHT?

THEIR NATURE... THEIR HEARTS...

THE VERY ROOT OF THEIR LIVES.

BASIC LEVEL?

LISTEN YOU! THIS ONE'S MINE!!

IF YOU DON'T EAT IT, WE WILL.

HUH?

SYAORAN-KUN?

WE CAN ORDER ANOTHER!

AH!

OKAY!

THESE "CHOPSTICKS" ARE HARD TO USE!

GRATCH

DOWN THE HATCH!

TUGG TUGG TUGG

...GREAT!!

風月

MMPRAAAAHH

THAT WAS...

GLARE

"TAKO-YAKI," FRIED OCTOPUS, IS REALLY GOOD, TOO!

IF YOU KNOW ANY OTHER GOOD PLACES, TELL US!

GOOD JOB GUIDING US HERE.

IT REALLY DID TASTE GOOD!

IT REALLY WAS.

OPEN

HELLO?
HELLO?
HELLO?

MOKONA WILL MAKE A PHONE CALL, TOO!

HE REALLY *DOES* WANT TO BE FRIENDS, HUH?

STARE

IT WAS ABOUT THAT CREATURE THAT APPEARED...

...THAT BEAST OF FIRE.

I NEARLY FORGOT.

OUR CONVERSATION WAS CUT OFF.

YOU WERE TALKING ABOUT YOUR DREAM...

YES...

I WANNA KNOW WHO THIS "SYAORAN" IS.

STAMP

ME, AS WELL.

IT WAS VERY PERSISTENT.

IF YOU'RE TALKING ABOUT DREAMS OF WEIRD ANIMALS... I HAD ONE, TOO.

34

SOST

HMP? Wa?

HMP Wa?

ZEEEEEEEEN

NOT A GOOD LISTENER, IS HE?

YAAAH!

YAAAH! TMP TMP

YAAAH!

TMP YAAAH!

TMP

YAAAH!

TUMP

I'VE BEEN PRETTY BORED HERE.

KRAKL

38

DOOM

I'LL TAKE YOU ON!

BUT...

...KUROGANE-SAN! YOU GAVE YOUR SWORD TO THAT WOMAN...

SHUT UP, OVER THERE!

THE HANSHIN REPUBLIC IS JUST HIS STYLE, HUH?

ZAPH

KURO-GANE'S BEEN LOOKING FORWARD TO THIS!

HE WASN'T BORED AT ALL!

BUT KUDAN...

...AREN'T MONSTERS.

THAT SWORD WAS MAGIC.

IT WAS SPECIAL.

I DON'T KNOW, AND I DON'T CARE.

HEH

SO... WHAT LEVEL IS *YOUR* KUDAN?

AND IN *MY* JAPAN, I NEEDED IT TO KILL THE MONSTERS THAT LIVED THERE.

WHAT'S ALL THE *TALK* FOR?

COME AND GET ME!

IT'S A TEAM THAT WANTS TO CONTROL THIS DISTRICT!

THEY'RE BATTLING SHÔGO'S TEAM OVER IT!

MASAYOSHI-KUN, DO YOU KNOW THIS GUY?

SYAORAN-KUN!!

IS THEIR LEADER ANY GOOD?

YAAAHH

YAAAHH

YAAAHH

TAKE A LOOK AT THE ATTACK OF A FIRST-LEVEL KUDAN!

EAT THIS!!

HE MAY NOT LOOK LIKE MUCH, BUT HIS KUDAN IS ONE OF THE FASTEST AROUND!

AND...

HIS KUDAN IS *FIRST LEVEL!*

43

MY KUDAN! MY K U D A A A N!!

YAAAA!! YAAAA!!

HANG IN THERE!

ARE YOU OKAY, BOSS?

TH-THE KID LIED!

HE *DID* FORM A TEAM!

YOU'RE A PART OF SYAORAN'S TEAM, AREN'T YOU?

WHEEZE

WHEEZE

I'M NOT ON *ANY-BODY'S* TEAM!

LISTEN ...

...IN MY LIFE, I'VE ONLY SERVED UNDER ONE PERSON!

Chapitre.8
The Country Where Gods Live

WE'RE BACK!

KACHAK

WERE YOU ABLE TO FIND ANY CLUES?

YES!

TMP TMP TMP

WE'RE BACK!

WE'RE BACK!

SST.

WELCOME. COME ON IN.

OH! YOU'RE ALL HERE!

HOW'D IT GO?

...BEFORE ANY OF THAT...

BUT...

MMMMM!

WHERE'S MY "WELCOME HOME" KISS?! ♥

HONEY !!

PUT IT HERE, BABE!

YOU *HAD* A REACTION, BUT IT DISAPPEARED.

I SEE...

57

THAT BEAST MUST HAVE BEEN YOUR KUDAN, SYAORAN-KUN.

THAT'S RIGHT.

WHAT A HUGE BUMP! ARASHI'S REALLY STRONG

BONG

THROB THROB

AND...

...JUST WHEN SYAORAN WAS IN TROUBLE, SOMETHING THAT LOOKED LIKE A BEAST OF FIRE SUDDENLY APPEARED.

AND KUROGANE'S KUDAN ALSO SEEMS STRONG!

IT SEEMS LIKE A PRETTY STRONG ONE, TOO!

WELL...

HOW DO YOU KNOW THAT?

...THAT KUDAN ARE AKIN TO GODS IN THIS NATION.

IT'S MY BELIEF...

I TOLD YOU BEFORE...

...I'M A SCHOLAR OF HISTORY.

THE KUDAN ARE THE LINCHPIN OF THE WHOLE THING.

IN THE HANSHIN REPUBLIC, THERE IS A MYTH THAT'S BEEN HANDED DOWN THROUGH THE AGES...

IT SAYS THAT THE NUMBER OF KAMI, GODS, IS "YAOYOROZU."

IT'S SPELLED WITH THE CHARACTERS FOR "EIGHT MILLION."

八百万 "YAOYOROZU"?

THEY SAY THERE ARE AS MANY GODS AS THERE ARE THINGS AND PHENOMENA IN THE WORLD.

THE WORD "YAOYOROZU" REALLY SIMPLY MEANS, "A WHOLE LOT."

NO, PROBABLY MANY MORE.

...KAMI-SAMA!

LOTS OF...

SO THERE ARE EIGHT MILLION GODS HERE?

59

THAT'S PRETTY IMPRESSIVE.

YOU LIVE TOGETHER WITH YOUR GODS.

SO THE GODS OF THAT MYTH ARE NOW CALLED KUDAN?

SO THE GODS OF THIS LAND ...

...PROTECT EACH AND EVERY PERSON WHO LIVES IN IT!

WHOOSH

YOU CAME TO THAT CONCLUSION, TOO?

THE KUDAN, OR RATHER THE GODS, HAVE A LASTING LOVE FOR THE PEOPLE OF THIS COUNTRY!

I'VE THOUGHT THAT ALL ALONG!

EVERY PERSON, WITHOUT EXCEPTION, IS ACCOMPANIED BY A KUDAN.

SO EVERY HUMAN IN THIS COUNTRY IS PROTECTED!

NOT ONE IS LEFT ALONE!

THEY HATE LOSING; THEY NEVER GET TO THE POINT; THEY'LL ATTACK IF YOU'RE NOT PAYING ATTENTION; IF OUR TEAM WINS THEY GO CRAZY; THEY THROW THEMSELVES IN THE RIVER...

IT'S TRUE...

...THAT A LOT OF PEOPLE IN THE HANSHIN REPUBLIC ARE EASY TO GET RILED UP.

... I THINK THEY REALLY ARE GOOD PEOPLE.

BUT EVEN SO ...

.....

YES.

... SEARCHING HERE IS PROBABLY BETTER THAN SEARCHING IN A COUNTRY FULL OF BAD PEOPLE; OR A COUNTRY THAT MAKES WAR ON ITS NEIGHBORS.

AND THAT'S WHY...

... WHEN IT COMES TO FINDING SAKURA'S FEATHER ...

SO IF IT WERE SIMPLY SOMEONE WHO HAD THE FEATHER AND WALKED AWAY...

...YOU PROBABLY COULD HAVE EASILY TRACKED DOWN WHERE IT WENT TO.

YOU SAID THAT YOU DETECTED THE WAVES OF SAKURA'S FEATHER, BUT YOU DON'T KNOW WHERE IT WENT?

UH-HUH.

BUT IF THE ONE THAT HAD IT COULD APPEAR AND DISAPPEAR...

...THE ONLY THING THAT COULD HAVE IT IS...

63

I WILL NEED THE HELP OF KUROGANE AND FAI.

TODAY WE HAVE BEEF UDON NOODLES AND FRIED TOFU SUSHI.

I MADE ALL THE ARRANGEMENTS BEFORE GOING OFF TO WORK.

ALL RIGHT!

SINCE WE'VE GOT THAT ALL DECIDED, IT'S TIME TO FORTIFY OURSELVES WITH SOME GOOD FOOD!

FSSH

YOU WERE AWAY FROM SAKURA ALL DAY.

YOU WERE WORRIED, WEREN'T YOU?

NOT TODAY, YOU DON'T.

MOKONA'S GOING TO EAT, SO MOKONA WILL WORK!

IF YOU DON'T WORK, YOU DON'T EAT.

WHY DO I HAVE TO HELP?

I'LL HELP TOO.

WHEN DINNER IS READY, I'LL GIVE YOU A CALL.

YOU CAN STAY AND WATCH HER.

KREEE

THANKS! THANKS A LOT!

KACHAK

68

WERE YOU ABLE TO FIND WHAT YOU WERE LOOKING FOR AFTER I LEFT?

HUFF WHEEZE
HUFF WHEEZE
WHOOSH

TMP TMP TMP

SYAORAN-KUN!!

MASA-YOSHI-KUN.

NOT YET...

THAT'S PRETTY AMAZING!

AMAZING! AMAZING!

BUT THAT'S ABOUT *ALL* HE CAN DO.

HE'S PRETTY WEAK!

MY KUDAN CAN FIND ANYBODY AS LONG AS HE'S MET THEM ONCE.

I'M SURPRISED YOU WERE ABLE TO FIND US.

IT'S NO GOOD IF IT'S TOO FAR AWAY, THOUGH.

ARE YOU SURE IT'S OKAY?

OKAY, THEN HOW ABOUT I BE YOUR GUIDE AGAIN TODAY?

BOING

SURE!

TODAY'S SUNDAY!

IT'S PERFECTLY FINE FOR TODAY!

74

Chapitre.9
The Magician's Kudan

76

BUT FOR SOME REASON, I DON'T UNDERSTAND THE WORDS!

NO, IT'S NOT THAT MY EARS HAVE GONE STRANGE.

AND IT'S NOT AS IF WE WENT ANYWHERE!

ABSOLUTELY CERTAIN, MA'AM!

HE WAS WITH THE SPIKY-HAIRED BIG GUY AND THE THIN BLOND GUY.

UMM...ARE YOU *SURE* THIS KID IS THE ONE?

THIS IS THE GUY SHÔGO SAID HE LIKED?

AND...

...THE SMALLEST ONE IN THE GROUP IS "SYAORAN."

HMMMM.

SKRICH
SKRICH

ЖЪФЛ

面倒
◎
！

I *KNEW* THEY WOULDN'T UNDER-STAND ME!

HANSHIN MAP

SUBWAY
HANSHIN CASTLE FRONT ENTRANCE STATION

HAN5
CAST

HANSHIN CASTLE IS THIS WAY!

TMP
TMP
TMP
TMP

WHOOM

ENTRANCE TO
HANSHIN CASTLE

MOKONA!

MASAYOSHI-KUN!

BULUUUUN

YOU LOOK LIKE YOU'RE HAVING *FUN!*

AT LEAST THE WHITE THING DOES!

HEEEEY!

HOW'D YOU GET UP THERE!?

SO IT *IS* MOKONA THAT'S DOING IT.

I GET IT NOW.

AT LEAST WHAT YOU TWO ARE SAYING.

YEAH.

SO YOU UNDER-STAND ME NOW?

82

MOKONA IS PRETTY INCREDIBLE!

TRANSPORTING US TO OTHER WORLDS...

TRANSLATING OUR LANGUAGES FOR US...

EATING APPLES WHOLE...

SWING, SWING, I'M JUST LIKE A BALLOON!

AND BLOW SOME MORE!

BLOW, WIND, BLOW!

MOKONA WAS SERVING AS A TRANSLATION DEVICE.

THAT'S WHAT IT MEANS.

HEY!

DOES THIS MEAN THAT ANY TIME WE GET SEPARATED FROM IT, WE WON'T BE ABLE TO COMMUNICATE?

TMP

WHAT A PAIN!!

AWW!

TMP TMP

TMP TMP

86

HOOWAAAAAA

Chapitre.10
Where the Feather Went

SWIP

EH?

LOOK UP THERE.

HUUUUU

VWAM

THAT WAS A SURPRISE.

A KUDAN CAN DO THAT?

YOU LIKED THAT ATTACK, DIDN'T YOU, MOKONA?

THIS COUNTRY IS PRETTY AMAZING.

PRIMERA-CHAN'S KUDAN IS SPECIAL LEVEL!

BE CAREFUL!

CLAP CLAP

KRAAAH!

AMAZING!

AMAZING!

96

97

LOOK AT THAT DAMN GRIN!

THAT MAN IS A COMBAT VETERAN.

BBB BOOM

THAT DOESN'T SURPRISE YOU?

I IMAGINE SO.

YEAAAH!

EH—?!

BBOOM

YEAAAH!

...THE LOOK IN HIS EYES JUST GIVES YOU THAT IMPRESSION.

THERE'S A CLUE IN THE CASUAL WAY FAI-SAN CARRIES HIMSELF...

...AND...

106

AND SINCE THIS GIRL IS FIGHTING WITH HER KUDAN, AND MOKONA ISN'T REACTING...

...IT MUST MEAN THAT THE GIRL ISN'T THE ONE WITH THE FEATHER.

I NEVER EXPECTED IT TO CHANGE FORM!

AND THOSE LETTERS SURE COME AFTER YOU!

PAT PAT

WHIRL, WHIRL.

SNIFF

TWIRL, TWIRL. I'M JUST LIKE A WATER BALLOON!

IF I DID, WHAT WOULD HAPPEN NEXT?

YEAH! YEAH!

DO YOU SURRENDER?

WELL?

AH HA HA!

SYAORAN-KUN HAS SOME IMPORTANT BUSINESS TO SEE THROUGH.

WE CAN'T HAVE THAT.

THEN I MOVE ON TO THE NEXT ONE TO DEFEAT, THIS "SYAORAN" GUY!

PRIMELA-CHAN!

PRIMELA-CHAN!

YEAAH!

YEAAH!

YEAAH!

I'D REALLY RATHER THAT IT ENDS WITH ME.

...THEN I...

IF SO...

HEH

SWUD

GWOOO

THUMP

WILL JUST HAVE TO WIIIIIIIN!!

Chapitre.11
The Kudan of Fire

RESERVoir CHRoNiCLE

IT'S THAT LEADER FROM BEFORE!

YOU'RE AN IDOL, RIGHT? DON'T YOU HAVE A CONCERT TO PREPARE FOR?

YOU'VE GOT WORK TO DO, RIGHT?

HMPH!

WHY ARE YOU DESTROYING OUR CULTURAL HERITAGE?!

EVEN IF IT IS...

BESIDES, THERE'S *PLENTY* OF TIME! THE CONCERT'S AT THE HANSHIN DOME RIGHT OVER THERE!

I DID IT BECAUSE... BECAUSE *YOU* NEVER COME TO SEE ME!

YOU DON'T! YOU DON'T!

THANK YOU!

DON'T BLAME ME IF THEY GET ALL MAD OVER IT!

VS KSH

117

WARAAAH

うわああんプリメラちゃん

PRIMERA-CHAN!!

SEE FOR YOUR-SELF!!

PAK

VWOOSH

WHO WOULD YOU MOST LIKE TO BE WITH?

On Your Days Off

HOW DO YOU KNOW?

BECAUSE PRIMERA-CHAN MADE IT OFFICIAL!

STAA

AARE

BUT SHE'S SOOO CUTE!!

でも可愛いんだよーっ!!

YOU'RE LOOKING IN THE WRONG PLACE! LOOK AT THE PHOTO SPREAD IN FRONT

少年マガジン

WEEKLY 25

TORA WATER

マガジン

うわうう哉

WARAAAAH!!

121

SORATA-SAN SAID THAT KUDAN PROTECT THEIR OWNERS.

SO PROBABLY, THE TIME THAT IT PUTS OUT ITS GREATEST STRENGTH IS WHEN IT'S PROTECTING ITS OWNER.

WHY ISN'T IT ONE FIXED STRENGTH?

BUT...

...IT GETS STRONGER AND THEN GETS WEAKER.

WHAT IS THAT SUPPOSED TO MEAN?

SO SOME KUDAN HAS TAKEN IT INSIDE ITSELF.

AND THAT MEANS...

...THE WAY TO FIND THE FEATHER IS THROUGH BATTLE!

FOWOOO!!

2000 KO!!

I GOT MY MONEY ON SYAORAN!

I BET 3000 KO ON SHOGO!

YOU GUYS, STAY OUTTA THIS, GOT ME?

READY!

POWER TO PROTECT SAKURA.

LIKE I SAID IN MY DREAM, I WANT POWER.

YOU'LL FIGHT ALONG-SIDE ME?

THAT WAS THE FIRST TIME I WAS EVER HIT LIKE THAT!

OH, MAN!

TUMP

PLIP
PLIP

FWA
SOOM

I'M FINE! I *TOLD* YOU TO STOP SCREAMING MY NAME!

YOU'LL RUIN YOUR VOICE JUST BEFORE A CONCERT!

SHÔGO-KUN!!

SHE'S SO CUTE!

DON'T TALK SO BIG! YOU'RE BREAKING STUFF TOO!

WHSSH

WH— WHO EVER SAID I *CARED* WHAT HAPPENS TO YOU?!

CUTE!

WHSSH

CHATTER

CHATTER

CHATTER

133

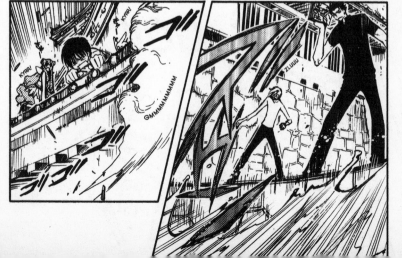

138

140

141

143

Chapitre.12
The Proof of Bravery

DID I HEAR RIGHT?

THE FEATHER'S IN THAT KUDAN?

IN *THAT* KUDAN?!

RMMMM

I THINK I SEE... EVEN WHEN HE USED HIS KUDAN TO FIND US, MOKONA DIDN'T DETECT IT.

BUT WHEN IT PROTECTS ITS MASTER...

THE TIME WHEN IT NEEDS THE MOST POWER IS WHEN IT IS PROTECTING SOMEONE IT CARES ABOUT FROM A LIFE-OR-DEATH SITUATION.

148

THE LAST TIME MOKONA DETECTED IT...

...WAS ALSO WHEN MASAYOSHI WAS IN A DANGEROUS SITUATION.

EVEN NOW, IT'S TRYING TO PROTECT HIM FROM THE CRUMBLING CASTLE.

YOU JUST PUT THAT BOY DOWN RIGHT NOW!

SHOOOO

BATTA BATTA

WABBY!

KRAKL

KRAKL

WOOOOO

SAKURA'S FEATHER...

...IS INSIDE THAT!

GO BACK TO *NORMAL* ALREADY!

H-HEY, I'M ALL RIGHT!

I'M JUST FINE!

THE FEATHER HAD TOO MUCH POWER FOR IT.

THAT'S MORE KUDAN THAN MASA-YOSHI CAN CONTROL.

WHAT'S WRONG WITH THAT KUDAN?

WHAT'LL YOU DO NOW?

STOP IT!!

WHOOSH

SYAORAN-KUN HAS STRENGTH.

IN A LOT OF DIFFERENT WAYS.

...WHY THAT FIRE KUDAN CAME TO HIM.

DOOO

I GET THE FEELING THAT I UNDERSTAND...

155

156

SYAORAN-
KUN!

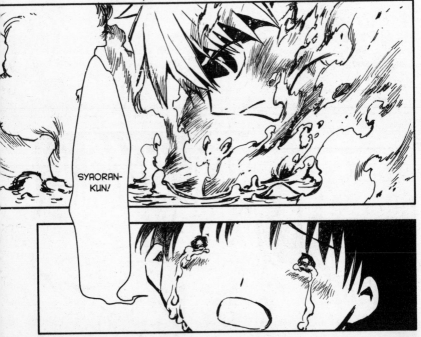

SYAORAN-
KUN!

H-HOT!!

AH!

161

T-TAKE IT!!

...THEN I WANT YOU TO HAVE IT!

IF THE THING INSIDE MY KUDAN IS THE THING YOU'RE LOOKING FOR...

MASAYOSHI-KUN!

SO IF IT BURNS ME, LET IT BURN!!

162

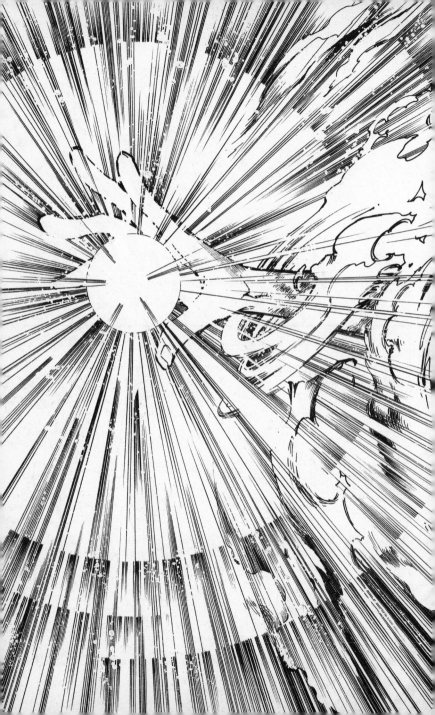

SHÔGO'S
KUDAN!

166

SHHHHHHHHH

THE *LEAST* I COULD DO WAS KEEP THE PLACE FROM CATCHING FIRE.

Chapitre.13
The Reason for Tears

170

AND AT THE MOMENT, YOU'VE LOST YOUR MEMORY. IT'S IN ORDER TO FIND YOUR MEMORIES THAT YOU'RE TRAVELING BETWEEN WORLDS.

ANOTHER... WORLD?

YOU ARE A PRINCESS FROM ANOTHER WORLD.

IF YOU'D BE SO KIND AS TO LISTEN, I'LL EXPLAIN.

YOU HAVE TRAVELING COMPANIONS.

NO...

BY MYSELF?

YES.

ARE YOU... ONE OF THOSE?

NICE TA MEETCHA!

SHAKE!

I'M KURO-GANE.

AND MAY I PRESENT—

MOKONA MODOKI! BUT YOU CAN SAY MOKONA!

SHUPP

AND THIS CUTE, FLUFFY ONE IS...

IT SEEMS ONE OF THE FEATHERS HAS BEEN RETURNED TO HER.

YES.

BUT IN THE PATHS TO COME, THERE IS NO GUARANTEE THAT THEY WILL BE AS LUCKY AS THEY WERE THIS TIME.

About the Creators

CLAMP is a group of four women who have become the most popular manga artists in America—Ageha Ohkawa, Mokona, Satsuki Igarashi, and Tsubaki Nekoi. They started out as doujinshi (fan comics) creators, but their skill and craft brought them to the attention of publishers very quickly. Their first work from a major publisher was *RG Veda*, but their first mass success was with *Magic Knight Rayearth*. From there, they went on to write many series, including *Cardcaptor Sakura* and *Chobits*, two of the most popular manga in the United States. Like many Japanese manga artists, they prefer to avoid the spotlight, and little is known about them personally.

CLAMP is currently publishing three series in Japan: *Tsubasa* and *xxxHOLiC* with Kodansha and *Gohou Drug* with Kadokawa.

Past Works

CLAMP have created many series. Here is a brief overview of one of them.

X/1999

Kamui Shirou left Tokyo after the death of the mother of his friends, Fuma and Kotori. Now, six years later, Kamui is confronted by a vision of his own mother's death. Burning, she commands him to seek his destiny in Tokyo, and so he returns.

A turning point for the planet Earth is coming in the year 1999. Ravaged by mankind's carelessness, the planet is polluted and near death. The priestess Hinoto has seen two possible visions for humanity: In one, mankind is saved, and in the other, mankind is destroyed so that the earth can be born anew. The Seven Seals, or Dragons of Heaven, are pledged to fight for the preservation of humanity. The Seven Minions, or Dragons of Earth, want to exterminate all human life to make way for a new age.

Hinoto's vision centers on Kamui, who has the power to choose the world's fate. Pledged to protect his childhood friends Fuma and Kotori, Kamui finds allies in the form of Arashi and Sorata, two of the Seven Seals. (You've already met the Hanshin-reality versions of Arashi and Sorata (Sora) in *Tsubasa* volume 1.) For the sake of his friends, Kamui chooses to fight for the Seven Seals. Sadly, Fuma is Kamui's "twin star," his opposite number, and because Kamui chose the side of good for himself, Fuma is forced to join the side of evil, the Seven Minions. Thus Kamui must fight the friend he sought to save.

Acknowledged as one of CLAMP's most visually stunning manga, *X/1999* is set in the same world as *CLAMP School Detectives* and *Tokyo Babylon*, and is still an ongoing series. The manga has been adapted as an anime film and a TV series.

Translation Notes

Japanese is a tricky language for most Westerners, and translation is often more art than science. For your edification and reading pleasure, here are notes on some of the places where we could have gone in a different direction in our translation of the work, or where a Japanese cultural reference is used.

Kyaa!

"Kyaaaa" is standard onomatopoeia (sound word) for a scream in manga, but many Japanese people have adopted this sound and use it to express joy, surprise, and other happy emotions.

Tsuruhashi

The town in which our heroes stop by to eat okonomiyaki (see next entry) is called Tsuruhashi. In our world, Tsuruhashi is only about a kilometer south of Osaka Castle, and it is the station which connects the Osaka Loop Line that circles the city with the Kintetsu-Nara line which goes out to the suburbs between Osaka and Nara. Millions of people pass through this station, and because of that, it's only natural that the restaurants there are both famous and good!

Okonomiyaki

They call it Japanese pancakes or Japanese pizza, but the only thing similar between those and okonomiyaki is that all are round and flat. Okonomiyaki

is made of flour, water, cabbage (mixed with other veggies), egg, seasonings, some kind of meat (seafood is common), and a delicious steak-sauce-like okonomiyaki sauce. The "konomi" means "like" or "love," and it indicates that you can put the veggies or meat you most like in it. The "yaki" means fried (the same as with "teriyaki" or "sukiyaki").

Flipping Rights

Most okonomiyaki that you will find in Japan is made in the kitchen, or at least, behind the counter. However, there are okonomiyaki restaurants where you can flip the okonomiyaki yourself. But since the dish was created in the Kansai (Osaka, Kyoto, Nara, Kobe) region, chefs jealously guard the right to flip their okonomiyaki—only when it's ready. After all, they are proud of their food and want it to be perfectly cooked.

Attack Names

Most anime, manga, and game fans are familiar with the attack names that the opponents shout at each other when making their attacks. Sure, it doesn't happen in real life, but it is a long-time entertainment convention. CLAMP was having a little crabby fun with the names of the attacks in this sequence.

KANI-NABE SENKAI!*

I THINK IF YOU TRY TO GET INVOLVED, HE'LL GET REALLY MAD.

KURO-TAN'S LIKE THAT.

Kuro-tan

The pet names that Fai always chooses for Kurogane aren't actually honorifics. Although they are similar in meaning to -chan, they are usually invented by young women who want to appear cute and add cute sounds to the names of people in their inner circle (close female friends and boyfriends). These syllables make the name sound almost babylike, and so Fai giving those names to gruff Kurogane is massively inappropriate, and as such, very funny.

THEY HATE LOSING; THEY NEVER GET TO THE POINT; THEY'LL ATTACK IF YOU'RE NOT PAYING ATTENTION; IF OUR TEAM WINS THEY GO CRAZY; THEY THROW THEMSELVES IN THE RIVER . . .

Drawbacks to Hanshin's People

Sorata's list of complaints about the people of the Hanshin Republic are common conceptions that Tokyoites have for the people of Osaka. Their stand-up comedy is famous for a Laurel and Hardy dynamic where one person says something dumb, and the other hits him over the head for it. And yes, they do throw themselves into the dirty, polluted river when the Hanshin Tigers win the national championship.

Kurogane's Language

Students of Chinese or Japanese may be able to make some sense out of Kurogane's language. The kanji in his word balloons are real, and if you look them up, you should be able to get some idea of what he is saying.

We Have a Winner!

The original sound effect here was "Pin-pon, pin-pon," the universal sound (in Japan) for a correct answer in a quiz show.

WHO IS THE ONE WHO WROTE THIS LETTER?!

Primera's Legion of Fans
Yes, CLAMP's depiction of Primera's fans is an exaggeration, but not by all that much...

"Is Everyone Having Fun?"
The Japanese phrase here is actually "Minna genki?" Similar to "Hello, Cleveland!" this is a standard phrase for a singer to say as a concert is beginning.

A TUDOR WHO TOOTED A *FRUIT* TRIED TO TUTOR TWO *DOODOOS* TO TOOT!

Tongue Twister I
Like English, Japanese has a large variety of tongue twisters, and here some of the more famous are misquoted by Primera. "Tonari no Kyaku wa yoku kaki kuu kyaku da" ("The guest next door eats a lot of persimmon"). But Primera said, "Tonari no gaki wa yoku kyaku kuu gaki da" ("The brat next door eats a lot of guests").

THE SIXTH SHEIK'S *SICKO'S* SHIP'S SUNK!

Tongue Twister 2

The tongue twister Primela wanted to say was, "Nama-mugi, nama-gome, nama-tamago" ("Raw barley, raw rice, raw egg"), but she got one word wrong. "Nama-gome" became "Nama-gomi" ("Raw garbage").

Tongue Twister 3

Primela tried to say, "Aka maki-gami, ao maki-gami, ki maki-gami" ("Red rolled paper, blue rolled paper, yellow rolled paper"), but she stumbled over the last words so it came out, "Maki-maki" ("rolled rolled").

RED LORRY, YELLOW LORRY, RED LORRY, YELLOW *YORRY!*

Tongue Twister 4

Primela was out of tongue twisters at this point, and she just started stringing words together like "pond skater," "red," and "aeiou."

A FLEA AND A FLY FLEW UP IN A FLUE, EE-AI-EE-AI-OH!

"Call me idiot!"

The word for fool, "baka," that many fans know already, is Tokyo dialect. A different word for fool, "aho," is Osaka dialect. Oddly, "aho" is not terribly insulting in Osaka, but "baka"

DON'T SAY "RETARD"! CALL ME A "FOOL" OR AN "IDIOT" IF YOU LIKE.

SHÔGO-KUN, ALL YOU CARE ABOUT ARE YOUR KUDAN BATTLES! YOU RETARD!

is, and the opposite is true in Tokyo. In the Japanese version, Primela called Shôgo "baka," and Shôgo replied, "At least say, 'Aho'!" He was noting that Primela was getting away from her Hanshin roots by using the word "baka."

Preview of

CLAMP

We are pleased to present to you a preview from Volume 3. Now available in bookstores everywhere.

CLAMP

TRANSLATED AND ADAPTED BY
William Flanagan

LETTERED BY
Dana Hayward

Tsubasa crosses over with *xxxHOLiC*. Although it isn't necessary to read *xxxHOLiC* to understand the events in *Tsubasa*, you'll get to see the same events from different perspectives if you read both!

Contents

Honorifics

Throughout the Del Rey Manga books, you will find Japanese honorifics left intact in the translations. For those not familiar with how the Japanese use honorifics, and more important, how they differ from American honorifics, we present this brief overview.

Politeness has always been a critical facet of Japanese culture. Ever since the feudal era, when Japan was a highly stratified society, use of honorifics — which can be defined as polite speech that indicates relationship or status — has played an essential role in the Japanese language. When addressing someone in Japanese, an honorific usually takes the form of a suffix attached to one's name (example: "Asuna-san"), or as a title at the end of one's name or in place of the name itself (example: "Negi-sensei," or simply "Sensei!").

Honorifics can be expressions of respect or endearment. In the context of manga and anime, honorifics give insight into the nature of the relationship between characters. Many translations into English leave out these important honorifics, and therefore distort the "feel" of the original Japanese. Because Japanese honorifics contain nuances that English honorifics lack, it is our policy at Del Rey not to translate them. Here, instead, is a guide to some of the honorifics you may encounter in Del Rey Manga.

-san: This is the most common honorific, and is equivalent to Mr., Miss, Ms., Mrs., etc. It is the all-purpose honorific and can be used in any situation where politeness is required.

-sama: This is one level higher than "-san." It is used to confer great respect.

-dono: This comes from the word "tono," which means "lord." It is an even higher level than "-sama," and confers utmost respect.

-kun: This suffix is used at the end of boys' names to express familiarity or endearment. It is also sometimes used by men among friends, or when addressing someone younger or of a lower station.

-chan: This is used to express endearment, mostly toward girls. It is also used for little boys, pets, and even among lovers. It gives a sense of childish cuteness.

Bozu: This is an informal way to refer to a boy, similar to the English term "kid" or "squirt."

Sempai: This title suggests that the addressee is one's "senior" in a group or organization. It is most often used in a school setting, where underclassmen refer to their upperclassmen as "sempai." It can also be used in the workplace, such as when a newer employee addresses an employee who has seniority in the company.

Kohai: This is the opposite of "sempai," and is used toward underclassmen in school or newcomers in the workplace. It connotes that the addressee is of lower station.

Sensei: Literally meaning "one who has come before," this title is used for teachers, doctors, or masters of any profession or art.

-[blank]: Usually forgotten in these lists, but perhaps the most significant difference between Japanese and English. The lack of honorific means that the speaker has permission to address the person in a very intimate way. Usually, only family, spouses, or very close friends have this kind of permission. Known as *yobisute*, it can be gratifying when someone who has earned the intimacy starts to call one by one's name without an honorific. But when that intimacy hasn't been earned, it can also be very insulting.

RESERVoir CHRoNiCLE

Chapitre.14
Time to Get Under Way

...WERE ALWAYS SO WEAK, SO...

BOTH MY KUDAN AND I...

MASA-YOSHI-KUN...

...I REALLY WANT TO THANK YOU.

EH HEH HEH

I'M GLAD YOU WERE ABLE TO GET THE FEATHER!

THAT ONE'S MINE!

SO...

PINNT

SO...

4

YOU AREN'T WEAK!

STRENGTH AND WEAKNESS AREN'T MEASURED ONLY IN BATTLE.

GOING OUT AND DOING YOUR BEST FOR SOMEONE ELSE'S SAKE...

...IS A WONDERFUL SIGN OF STRENGTH.

THANKS!

THANK YOU!

GWI

YO.

SHÔGO-SAN!!

EH?!

AHHH!

I'LL HAVE FUTA-MODAN.

AND A TORA-COLA.

OH! IT'S BEGINNING TO BURN. YOU'D BETTER EAT IT.

OF COURSE, SIR.

'SCUSE ME, WE'RE READY TO ORDER. I'LL HAVE TONPEI-YAKI!

I'M GLAD MY TEAM GETS GOOD INTELLIGENCE.

CAN YOU SKOOCH OVER A BIT?

I TOLD YOU TO STOP THAT!!

STAAARE

ONE FUTA-MODAN FOR THIS GENTLEMAN, YOUR MAJESTY!

YOUR MAJESTY?!

YOUR MAJESTY, REALLY?!

YOUR MAJESTY!

6

YAAAAAH!

BOINK

BOW

IT'S OKAY.

IT WAS THE ONLY THING YOU COULD DO, CIRCUM-STANCES BEING WHAT THEY WERE.

I'M SORRY TO HAVE INTERRUPTED YOUR BATTLE.

NOBODY GOT WOUNDED, RIGHT?

WE'RE FINE.

BOOO!

BOOO!

BOOO!

BOOO!

BOOO!

I LOST 3000 TORA ON THAT!

I WON!

OH, SHUT UP!

BESIDES, I WAS LOSING THAT BATTLE BADLY.

MOKONA, I THINK YOUR TAIL IS A LITTLE BURNT.

KUROGANE IS TERRIBLE! HE MADE MOKONA GO "BOINK" FROM THE HEAT!

YOU STOLE MY FOOD AGAIN!

YOU LITTLE SLUG!

WE'LL HAVE TO GO TO A NEW WORLD... ERR... COUNTRY VERY SOON.

I SEE...

HOW LONG WILL YOU BE IN THE HANSHIN REPUBLIC?

SST

I'D HOPED TO MEET YOU IN OTHER PLACES THAN JUST BATTLE.

I WANTED TO GUIDE YOU AROUND TOWN A BIT.

PRIMELA WAS DISAPPOINTED, TOO.

GLNCH

10

I SURE WILL!!

SHU

LOOM

GWAAAHH

SO THOSE WERE THE ONES THAT YÛKO-SAN WAS COUNTING ON.

YOU KNOW, I THINK THEY CAN OVERCOME ANY HARDSHIP THEY MAY FIND.

YES.

16

SHA-KOW

Chapitre.15
The Secret Country

I DON'T SEE ANYBODY STUPIDER THAN YOU.

WHO ARE YOU CALLING STUPID?!

I AM THE ONLY SON OF THE RYANBAN-SAMA, THE MASTER OF THE COUNTRY OF KORYO *INCLUDING* THE TOWN OF RYONFI!

YOU INSULT ME?!

YOU LITTLE...

DO YOU KNOW THE PUNISHMENT FOR OPPOSING THE RYANBAN?!

YOU DARE PUT DOWN MY FATHER?!

CHU'NYAN?!

YOU MAY *CALL* HIM RYAN-BAN ...

...BUT LESS THAN A YEAR AGO, HE WAS JUST A WANDERING SHINBAN MAGICIAN!

ARE YOU HURT?

I'M JUST FINE.

SHMP

SHMP

GRUMBLE
GRUMBLE

JUST BE PREPARED!

I CLAIM THE RIGHT OF RETRIBUTION FOR THESE INSULTS!

THANK YOU!

WHAT IS ALL THIS?

SYAORAN WAS *GREAT!*

JUMPING AROUND!

SHMP

SHMP

JMMP

WELL...

...IT LOOKS LIKE WE MADE A SPLASH IMMEDIATELY AFTER OUR ARRIVAL.

26

LOOK AT THESE GUYS!

RUNNING AMOK IN OUR MARKET!

I CAN ONLY WISH THAT AMEN'OSA WOULD COME TO TOWN AS QUICKLY AS THEY CAN.

THOSE ARE WEIRD CLOTHES!

28

STARE

HUSH

SH.

SH

WHY DID YOU SUDDENLY...

MY HOUSE.

UM... WHERE ARE...

DON'T YOU HAVE SOMETHING TO SAY?

30

IT'S MITO-KÔMON!!

BOYOIING

MITO...?

JUST THINK OF MOKONA AS A MASCOT.

OR MAYBE AN IDOL.

MOKONA IS MOKONA!!

BYOIING

WR... AH!

WOBBLE

YÛKO SAYS THAT THE FIRST GUY WHO PLAYED KÔMON-SAMA IS THE BEST!!

HA HA HA HA HA

B-BMP B-BMP

I'VE BEEN WONDERING THIS FOR A WHILE, BUT... WHAT IS THAT THING?

WHY WOULD A MANJU STEAMED BUN SPEAK?

MOKONA'S AN IDOL!

MMMM!

RUBB RUBB RUBB

CHU'NYAN.

SO YOU THINK WE'RE THIS AMEN'OSA OF YOURS...

UM...

33

AND FINALLY... THIS IS KURO-PUU!

黒鋼

KURO-PUU!

THAT'S "KUROGANE"!!

CHU'NYAN-CHAN, HUH? MY NAME'S FAI.

春香ちゃんね

AND...

THIS IS SYAORAN-KUN.

WE HAVE SAKURA-CHAN OVER HERE.

...FOR YOU TO WISH THAT THIS AMEN'OSA WERE TO COME, YOU MUST THINK THIS LEADER OF YOURS IS A BAD MAN.

IN OTHER WORDS...

HE TOOK MY OMONI... MY MOTHER, AND...

HE'S THE WORST!

FSSH

WHROOGH

KRRKK

KRAKK

KRAKK

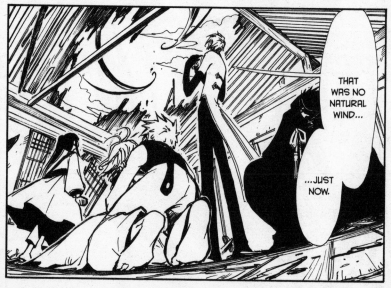

THAT WAS NO NATURAL WIND...

...JUST NOW.

38

YES...

FATHER!
ABOJI!
YOU
DID IT!

40

NOW THE TOWN OF RYONFI KNOWS THE POWER OF ITS RYANBAN!

BUT WHO DO YOU THINK THOSE PEOPLE ARE?

ABOJI?

YAY!

THEY COULDN'T REALLY BE AMEN'OSA, COULD THEY?

41

Chapitre.16
Empty Memory

RESERVoir CHRoNiCLE

45

IS IT ALL RIGHT TO TAKE THE PRINCESS OUT LIKE THIS?

YOU NEVER KNOW IF SHE'S ROWING THE BOAT OR ASLEEP AT THE OAR.

AWW, DAMMIT!

WHY DOES THAT STUPID MANJU BUN HAVE TO BE ON THAT BRAT'S SHOULDER ALL THE TIME?!

HA HA HA HA!

CHU'NYAN-CHAN OFFERED TO TAKE SAKURA-CHAN AND SYAORAN-KUN ON A RECONNAIS-SANCE MISSION.

MOKONA MIGHT BE ABLE TO SENSE SOMETHING.

SHE'S ONLY BEEN ABLE TO RETRIEVE TWO FEATHERS.

EVEN THOUGH IT *DOES* SEEM THAT A FEW MEMORIES HAVE RETURNED.

SHE DOESN'T HAVE ENOUGH MEMORIES YET...

...TO RETURN TO THE OLD SAKURA-CHAN AGAIN.

46

HE'S GOING TO TRAVEL ALL THE WORLDS AND FIND SAKURA-CHAN'S SCATTERED FRAGMENTS OF MEMORY...

BUT SYAORAN-KUN'S STILL SEARCHING...

...ISN'T HE?

...NO MATTER HOW PAINFUL IT WILL BE FOR HIM IN THE END.

SO...

IN ANY CASE, IT'S OUR JOB TO MAKE REPAIRS WHILE WAITING FOR THEM TO COME HOME.

I WONDER IF THEY'LL BRING PRESENTS?

HM?

WHERE DOES THAT GIVE YOU THE RIGHT TO RELAX AND DRINK TEA?!

おまえも ヤレよ!!

GET TO WORK!!

BUT...

...I'M SUPERVISING KURO-PIPPI'S HARD WORK!

SLUMP

DO YOU FEEL A POWER WAVE FROM A FEATHER?

MOKONA CAN'T TELL.

うーーーん

MMMM

MMMM

う

The Country of
KORYO

"WEIRD POWER"?

THROUGH THIS WHOLE COUNTRY...

...MOKONA FEELS IT FILLED WITH A WEIRD POWER!

50

HO, CHU'NYAN!

YOU'RE DRAGGING AN OUTSIDER AROUND TOWN, HUH?

I'VE SEEN SOMETHING VERY MUCH THE SAME AT ONE POINT.

THEY'RE CALLED "SAIKORO" WHERE I COME FROM.

IT'S CALLED NEGI.

DON'T YOU KNOW ABOUT IT?

WHAT IS THIS?

OHO! TRAVELERS!

WILL YOU JOIN US?

THEY'RE GUESTS!

THEY CAME FROM A LONG WAY AWAY!

AND IF THEY ADD UP TO HAVE MORE DOTS THAN YOUR OPPONENT, YOU WIN!

THROW TWO CUBES.

IT'S EASY!

AAH! IT TALKED!!

WHAT IS THIS?!

MOKONA!!

THEY JUST LOVE THIS GAME! HONESTLY!

THE OLDER MEN DO, ANYWAY!

THEN... WHO IS THE PERSON WHO THREW THE HIGHEST NUMBER?

NOW...

...TEST YOUR LUCK!

KLIK KLAK

WHY NOT?

ALL I REMEMBER ...

...IS MY NAME ...

... AND ...

...SOME PEOPLE FROM A DESERT TOWN.

THAT'S ALL.

BEYOND THAT, I CAN'T REMEMBER A THING.

THAT'S ABOUT ALL.

...BUT THERE WAS A LITTLE BIT OF LOVINGLY TENDED LAND.

THERE WAS DESERT ALL AROUND US...

I'M SORRY. I DIDN'T MEAN TO ASK ANYTHING SO PAINFUL TO ANSWER.

HIM... UM...

SYAORAN-KUN TOLD ME.

THE REASON WE'RE TRAVELING NOW IS TO REGAIN MY MEMORIES.

I DON'T KNOW ANY-THING OF IT REALLY...

AHHH!

...BUT HE TOLD ME ALL ABOUT IT.

UM... SYAORAN-KUN?

IS IT OKAY IF I CALL YOU JUST "SYAORAN"?

YOUR STORE HASN'T PAID THE RYANBAN'S TAX MONEY, HAS IT?!

DON'T! PLEASE!!

MY FATHER IS OLD AND SICK! AND A SICK HARABOJI NEEDS HIS MEDICINE!

ALL I ASK IS FOR YOU TO WAIT A LITTLE WHILE LONGER!

NO MORE WAITING!!

YOU'RE CHARGING TWENTY TIMES WHAT THE OLD RYANBAN CHARGED!

THERE'S NO WAY WE CAN PAY THAT!

WE CAN'T!

YOU WILL PAY ALL OF THE TAXES YOU OWE IN FULL NOW!!

61

SHE HAD PRIDE IN HER JOB AS A SHINBAN!

BUT SHE WOULD NEVER HAVE USED THAT POWER FOR BAD PURPOSES!

PEOPLE WOULD ASK HER TO MAKE MEDICINES OR CAST CHARMS.

SHE HAD SOME WONDERFUL POWERS!

BUT THAT CREEP AND HIS FATHER...

THEN THEY CHASED THE OLD RYANBAN-SAMA AWAY AND SET THEMSELVES UP AS RYANBAN IN HIS PLACE!

THEY DIDN'T HAVE ANY SPECIAL POWERS, BUT SUDDENLY THEY BECAME VERY POWERFUL!

THEY WERE JUST WANDERING SHINBAN THAT CAME TO TOWN A YEAR AGO!

Chapitre.17
The Source of Magic

68

ZLISTS

STMP

STMP

HE
DID
IT!!

DON'T
LET IT GO
TO YOUR
HEAD!

70

WHUMP

SYAORAN-KUN!!

PLIP
PLIP

YOU GET IT NOW?!

THIS IS THE POWER OF THE RYANBAN!

JUST *SHUT UP!!*

YOU HAVE TO CALL FOR YOUR DADDY WHEN YOU'RE LOSING A FIGHT?!

YOU ARE THE WORST EXCUSE FOR A FAMILY I'VE EVER SEEN!

IF YOU DON'T LIKE IT, THEN GO AHEAD AND TRY TO BEAT MY ABOJI, CHU'NYAN!!

BUT YOU *CAN'T!*

WHY?

BECAUSE YOU CAN'T EVEN *TOUCH* HIM!!

YAP AWAY ALL YOU WANT!

WHEN AMEN'OSA COMES, ALL OF THE EVIL THINGS THAT YOU TWO HAVE BEEN DOING WILL BE JUDGED!

YOU CAN'T—

AS PUNISHMENT FOR YOUR RESISTANCE, YOUR TAX IS DOUBLED!

IF YOU DON'T PAY, YOUR STORE WILL BE CONFISCATED, AND YOU AND THE OLD MAN WILL RECEIVE 300 LASHES!

THEY'LL NEVER COME!

H HEH!

WELCOME HOME! HOW DID EVERYTHING GO?

THE FACT THAT I WAS ABLE TO TALK TO KURO-TAN THE WHOLE TIME MEANS THAT YOU MUST HAVE STAYED PRETTY NEARBY.

HMMP

THUNK

I GUESS SOMETHING IS WRONG.

IS SOMETHING WRONG?

BUT...

...IF THE RYANBAN IS THIS BAD, WHY HAVEN'T YOU RISEN UP AGAINST HIM?

PWP

I SEE...

YOU WERE DEFEATED BY THE WIND OF THIS RYANBAN GUY AGAIN.

WE DID TRY... A NUMBER OF TIMES.

A GREAT NUMBER OF TIMES!

THE RYANBAN'S CASTLE HAS SOME KIND OF MAGIC AROUND IT.

NOBODY WAS ABLE TO GET CLOSE.

BUT WE WERE NEVER ABLE TO SET ONE FINGER ON THE RYANBAN.

BY MY WAY OF THINKING, THAT IDEA IS A LITTLE LATE IN COMING.

HAVE YOU CONSIDERED HOLDING HIM HOSTAGE OR SOMETHING LIKE THAT?

WHAT ABOUT THAT SON OF HIS?

THAT MAKES SENSE!

なるほど!

THAT ACCOUNTS FOR THE WEIRD POWER THAT MOKONA SENSED, DOESN'T IT?

WITH ALL OF THE WEIRD POWER AROUND, MOKONA CAN'T TELL IF THERE IS A POWER WAVE FROM THE FEATHER OR NOT.

コク コク

NOD NOD

NOW YOU'RE TALKING!

EHP!?

THAT WOULDN'T ADD UP.

IT WAS ONLY A SHORT TIME AGO THAT THE MEMORY FEATHERS WERE SCATTERED THROUGH THE WORLDS.

WE'RE IN DIFFERENT DIMENSIONS.

IT'S POSSIBLE THAT TIME FLOWS DIFFERENTLY IN EACH OF THEM.

SYAORAN-KUN, YOU'RE WOUNDED!

BUT...

I'M FINE!

WAIT!

I'LL GO CHECK...

...ON WHETHER THE RYANBAN HAS A FEATHER OR NOT.

79

JUST WAIT A MOMENT.

THE MAGIC OF THE RYANBAN IS PRETTY STRONG.

IF YOU SIMPLY WALK THERE, YOU'LL NEVER SUCCEED.

AT THE VERY LEAST, WE'LL NEED ENOUGH POWER TO CREATE AN ENTRANCE TO THAT CASTLE.

AH, NO...

YOU CAN RELAX.

IT'S JUST...

I'M NOT TRYING TO STOP YOU.

MOKONA WILL ASK!!

QUIT PRETENDING YOU HAVE A PLAN WHEN YOU DON'T!!

WHO? THE SPACE-TIME WITCH?

IMPOSSIBLE!

VSSH

CAN'T *YOU* DO SOMETHING ABOUT THAT?

MOKONA SURE IS CONVENIENT AT TIMES!

WE CAN TALK TO DIFFERENT DIMENSIONS!

THERE ARE LIMITS TO HOW CONVENIENT THINGS SHOULD BE!!

SEEP?!

I SEE.

SO YOU HAVE TO BREAK THROUGH THE MAGIC— IF THAT'S WHAT IT IS— TO ENTER THE CASTLE?

THAT'S THE PROBLEM.

THE MARKINGS THAT MADE UP YOUR PAYMENT TO ME...

...WERE A DEVICE THAT HELD YOUR MAGICAL POWER IN CHECK.

WHY WOULD YOU NEED TO CONTACT ME?

FAI CAN USE MAGIC, CAN'T HE?

I TURNED OVER THE SOURCE OF MY MAGIC TO YOU.

84

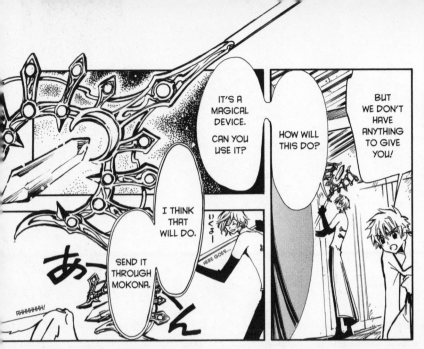

IT'S A MAGICAL DEVICE.

CAN YOU USE IT?

HOW WILL THIS DO?

BUT WE DON'T HAVE ANYTHING TO GIVE YOU!

I THINK THAT WILL DO.

SEND IT THROUGH MOKONA.

HERE GOES...

AHHHHHH!

AAAAAH!

AAAAAAH!

GULP

ARE YOU SURE?

YES... I'M SURE.

BOINK

SLOOM

THIS...

...WILL DEFEAT THE CASTLE'S MAGIC?

POP

86

Chapitre.18
The Castle of Traps

88

90

...IS BECAUSE SHE'S ALREADY SUFFERED TOO MUCH HARDSHIP.

THE REASON YOU'RE NOT TAKING CHU'NYAN ALONG...

I THINK YOU SHOULD HAVE SAID IT.

I DON'T HAVE ANY STRONG MAGIC...

...AND IF FOR SOME REASON WE AREN'T ABLE TO DEFEAT THE RYANBAN, CHU'NYAN WILL SUFFER THE WORST FOR IT.

THE RYANBAN SAW THAT SHE TOOK IN STRANGERS LIKE US, AND IF WE BROUGHT HER TO STORM THE CASTLE...

.....

WHAT HAPPENS IF WE FIND OUT THAT THE RYANBAN DOES HAVE ONE OF SAKURA'S FEATHERS?

SO....

WHAT-EVER ELSE HAPPENS...

...AND PUT HIM OUT OF OUR MISERY!

...IT'LL BE BETTER IF WE TAKE THE RYANBAN...

HEH

92

I'LL GET IT BACK!

I WONDER WHAT THAT CHILD HAS HIDDEN?

THOSE FOOLS!

LET THEM COME!

I SENSE A STRONG POWER.

SO, THEY'VE COME.

D—

DON'T WORRY, ABOJI!

NO ONE CAN STAND AGAINST YOUR MAGIC!

94

AAHH!!

WEIRD! WEIRD!

THE CLOUDS ARE BELOW THE GROUND!

SO *THIS*...

VITT

IT WON'T BE JUST THIS GATE.

I IMAGINE THAT ALL OF THE CASTLE GATES WILL BE THE SAME.

CHU'NYAN-CHAN *DID* SAY THAT THE CASTLE WAS PROTECTED BY MAGIC.

YOU'RE TOO IMPATIENT, KURO-MIN!

SHUT UP!

VOING

YOU THROW IT!!

EH?!

...IS THE TIME FOR THE ITEM GIVEN TO US BY THE SPACE-TIME WITCH.

TA-DAAAAAAH

IT LOOKS LIKE A MUDBALL.

YOU THROW IT AS HARD AS YOU CAN!

HOW'RE WE SUPPOSED TO USE THIS THING?

HARD ENOUGH TO HIT THE CASTLE!

DOOOM

WHAT KIND OF PLANS ARE THEY MAKING?

SURE! THAT'LL WORK!

MOKONA, IF I HAVE TO GET IT THAT FAR...

AA?

EHEH

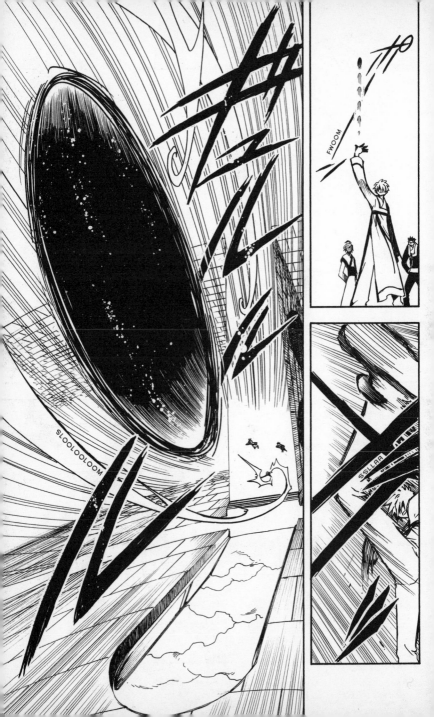

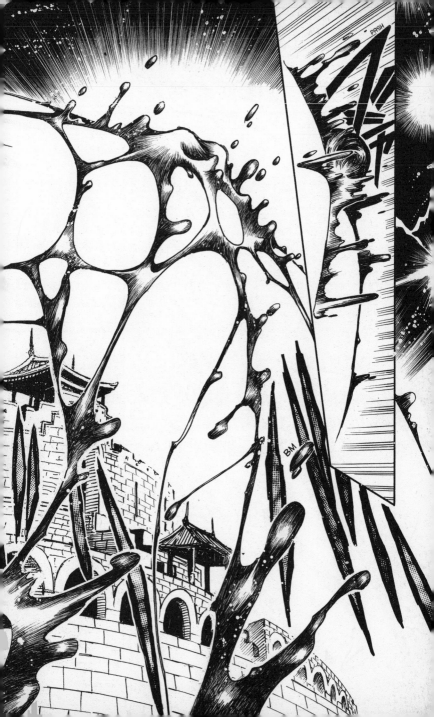

WE'RE BACK WHERE WE STARTED.

I DROPPED THIS ON THE FLOOR AT A SPOT NOT FAR FROM THE ENTRANCE.

I KNOW THIS PLACE LOOKS FAMILIAR, BUT WE NEVER TURNED AROUND!

HM?

IT'S BEEN A ONE-WAY TRIP.

YOU SAID THE WORDS "WHEET-WHOO." YOU DIDN'T WHISTLE.

I'VE BEEN WONDERING ABOUT THAT.

SORRY, BUT I DON'T KNOW HOW TO WHISTLE.

EH HEH HEH

WHOOO

THAT WAS ONE OF THE STONES OF THE GAME THAT FAI AND KUROGANE WERE PLAYING AT CHU'NYAN'S HOUSE!

WHEET-WHOO!

SYAORAN-KUN, YOU'RE GOOD.

101

NOW, KUROGANE-CHI MIGHT BE ABLE TO RELIEVE SOME OF HIS STRESS BY BREAKING THROUGH IT.

BUT THERE'S A VERY STRONG MAGIC POWER IN THIS DIRECTION.

I CAN FEEL IT... I THINK.

I DON'T KNOW FOR SURE.

YOU'RE NOT GONNA USE YOUR GREAT MAGIC POWERS?

I WOULDN'T SO MUCH CALL IT MAGIC.

IT'S MORE LIKE INTUITION.

たた TUMP

たた TUMP

105

Chapitre.19
The Strongest Kiishim

...BUT IT'S BEEN SO LONG SINCE I HAD A GUEST, I'LL FORGIVE YOUR COARSE TONE.

YOU HUMANS— PATHETIC CREATURES WITH LIVES SPANNING LESS THAN A HUNDRED YEARS— YOU'RE NO BETTER THAN WORMS!

SUCH CREATURES SHOULD WATCH THEIR TONGUES.

OR SO I SHOULD SCOLD YOU...

WHAT IS SHE SPOUTING?

HUH?

あ...!?

WHO THE HELL ARE YOU?!

BOTH SHORT-TEMPERED AND SHY! THE COMBO'S PRETTY CUTE!

KURO-BUN, YOUR TEMPER IS A LITTLE *TOO* QUICK HERE!

THIS IS SUCH A PAIN!

WHATEVER! JUST COUGH UP THE LOCATION OF THAT RYANBAN OF YOURS!

SHE'S CALLING US KIDS!!

TEH HEH

WHAT A NICE COMPLIMENT!

WHAT AMUSING CHILDREN!

I THINK THAT SOMETHING I'M SEARCHING FOR IS IN THIS CASTLE.

WILL YOU PLEASE TELL ME WHERE THE RYANBAN IS?

I LIKE THE LOOK IN YOUR EYES.

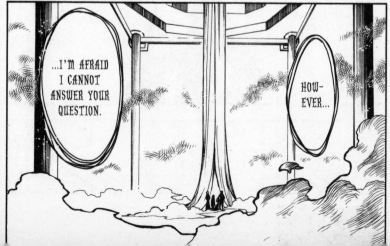

...I'M AFRAID I CANNOT ANSWER YOUR QUESTION.

HOW- EVER...

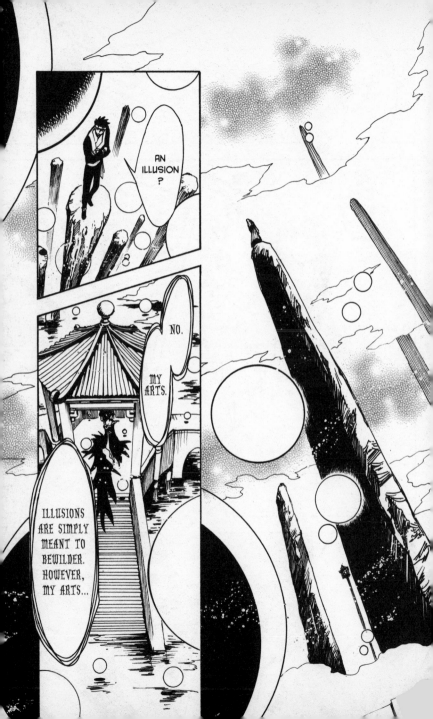

117

118

WE'RE NOT FINISHED WITH THE BATTLE HERE!

SYAORAN-KUN...

...TAKE MOKONA AND GO ON AHEAD.

NOW...

...WE'LL NEVER GET ANYWHERE PLAYING IN THIS PLAYGROUND.

YOU HAD BETTER MOVE FORWARD WHILE YOUR LEG STILL WORKS.

ALSO...

TRUE.

BUT NUMBERS WON'T HELP IN THIS BATTLE.

SYAORAN-KUN, YOU STILL HAVE UNFINISHED BUSINESS, HAVEN'T YOU?

NEVER FEAR!

KURO-PII WILL SAVE THE DAY FOR US!

THANK YOU!

POFF

ME AGAIN?!

THE MAGIC IS THINNEST ABOVE US.

SYAORAN-KUN, NO DOUBT YOU'LL BE ABLE TO MAKE IT OUT THAT WAY.

121

I'LL HAVE TO TREAT THE TWO REMAINING CHILDREN WITH MOXIBUS- TION.

.....

HUMPH!

I'D SAY OUR SITUATION IS SERIOUS.

IF THAT'S THE CASE...

SYAORAN!

DOES YOUR FOOT HURT?

IT'S FINE.

ZLIP

DOOM

I'M GONNA HAVE TO MAKE SURE YOU CAN NEVER STAND AGAIN!!

Chapitre.20
The Final Battle

RESERVoir CHRoNiCLE

THAT'S RIGHT!

I SENSE THAT WEIRD FEELING FROM HIM REALLY STRONGLY!

MY ABOJI, THE RYANBAN OF RYONFI TOWN AND THE COUNTRY OF KORYO, GAVE ME THIS BODY!

THE SECRET ARTS, HUH?

YOU UPSTART LITTLE *BRAT!!*

MOKONA, STAY BACK A WAY.

SYAORAN!

WHOOO

WHOOM

KRMBL

KRMBL

133

THAK

SPASSH

I SEE YOUR POINT.

NEXT TIME YOU MOVE ME, DO IT WITH A LITTLE MORE CARE, HM?

IF I DIDN'T, YOU'D BE MELTED BY NOW.

KURO-MU! YOU'RE MEAN!

KAFF

KAFF

SHHHHHHH

YOU HAVE SOME SKILL, CHILDREN.

BOK

JANNG

IT'S BEEN ...

BOK

140

141

144

SO WE'D BETTER STEP IT UP, AND GET TO OUR NEXT WORLD.

AND WE'RE NOT GOING ANYWHERE UNTIL THAT WHITE MANJU BUN FINDS THE PRINCESS'S FEATHER, RIGHT?

...WILL PROBABLY COME AFTER ME.

BECAUSE THERE IS A PERSON SLEEPING UNDER-WATER WHO, WHEN HE WAKES UP...

WHY'S THAT?

PERSONALLY, I DISLIKE STAYING IN ONE PLACE.

SO, I HAVE TO RUN...

...TO AS MANY WORLDS AS I CAN FIND.

HAVE YOU FINISHED YOUR FINAL WORDS?

HMP?

?

.....

HEY!

DESPERATE TIMES... AS THE SAYING GOES. AH HA HA!

NOW...

...WHAT DO WE DO?

GATCH

KYAAA!

WHAT THE HELL IS THIS THING?!

DID YOU CONJURE IT UP WITH MAGIC?!

S Y A O R A N !

S Y A O R A N !

THE RUMORS...

...TALK ABOUT THERE BEING PEOPLE IN AMEN'OSA THAT CAN USE MAGIC!

BUT YOU GUYS DON'T REALLY CALL YOURSELVES AMEN'OSA, DO YOU?

152

153

THE KIISHIM...

...WOUNDED YOU IN THIS FOOT, DIDN'T SHE?

IS IT AGONIZING?

WELL?

DOES IT HURT?!

IT ISN'T THERE AS GUARD.

YOU AREN'T GONNA BEAT SOMEBODY AS GOOD AS I AM PUTTING UP A WOUNDED LEG AS YOUR GUARD.

YOU LIKE TO USE KICKS WHEN YOU FIGHT.

154

GRR...

THE KIISHIM SHOULD *NEVER* HAVE BEEN DEFEATED!

MY SON...

HE SHOULD BE FINISHING UP HIS JOB BY NOW...

160

IF YOU TRY ANY MORE OF YOUR WEIRD TRICKS...

JANNG

INSIDE THAT STONE WERE THE MAGICS THAT KEPT ME IN THRALL TO THE RYANBAN.

THAT WAS A THANK YOU.

WHAT KIND OF MAGIC ARE YOU TRYING ON ME NOW?!

HAD I THE CHOICE, I WOULD NEVER HAVE DEFENDED THAT BRAINLESS RYANBAN AND HIS SON AGAINST TWO SUCH STEADFAST CHILDREN.

I WAS FINALLY SET FREE.

OH! I SEE.

あー なるほど

AND WHEN KURO-PON SMASHED THE STONE...

AND THE RYANBAN CUR IS ATTEMPTING TO ATTACK WITH...

...YET ANOTHER COWARDLY TACTIC.

HOWEVER, IT SEEMS THAT THE SMALLEST OF YOU CHILDREN HAS ALREADY ARRIVED.

YOU WISHED TO KNOW THE LOCATION OF THE RYANBAN.

HE ABIDES IN THE HIGHEST FLOOR OF THE CASTLE.

ARE
YOU
HERE
...

... MOKONA
?

YEAH
...

THIS
IS WHERE
THE WEIRD
POWER IS
STRONGEST.

BUT
MOKONA'S
FEELING
REALLY
DIZZY...

KREEEEEE

IT'S SAKURA'S FEATHER!

YOU WERE ABLE TO DEFEAT MY MAGIC!

THEN YOU *MUST* BE AMEN'OSA.

BOINK

.....
LET THEM DOWN.

WAIT...

EVEN IF THEY DID, THERE'S STILL A GOOD CHANCE THAT I CAN DEFEAT AMEN'OSA, TOO.

SO THEY TOLD THE CENTRAL GOVERN-MENT ABOUT ME.

168

169

Chapitre.21
*The Mirror of the
Greatest Love*

IF YOU ATTACK THESE TOWNS-MEN...

...YOUR TWO YOUNG WOMEN WILL FEEL THEIR PAIN MANY TIMES OVER!!

172

173

174

175

WHAT WAS THAT?

THAT'S JUST A TRICK, TOO?

DOESN'T CALL ME "SYAORAN."

WH—

WHAT ARE YOU SAYING?

THEY'RE THE TRUE—

HER HIGH- NESS...

YOUR HOSTAGES UP THERE ARE JUST FAKES, AREN'T THEY?

AH!

PLAYTIME IS OVER.

KRA-KOW

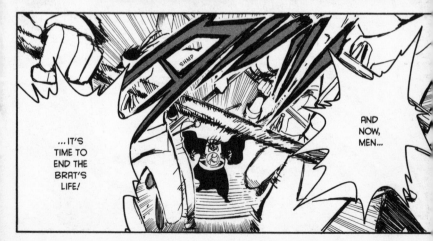

...IT'S TIME TO END THE BRAT'S LIFE!

AND NOW, MEN...

WHAT'S THIS?

IT SEEMS PRETTY CROWDED IN THERE.

GIVE THE FEATHER BACK!

YOU'RE BOTH *LATE!!*

ZOOM

AW, SHADDUP!

IT SEEMS THAT QUITE A BIT HAS GONE ON HERE.

SORRY.

186

188

To Be Continued

About the Creators

CLAMP is a group of four women who have become the most popular manga artists in America—Ageha Ohkawa, Mokona, Satsuki Igarashi, and Tsubaki Nekoi. They started out as doujinshi (fan comics) creators, but their skill and craft brought them to the attention of publishers very quickly. Their first work from a major publisher was *RG Veda*, but their first mass success was with *Magic Knight Rayearth*. From there, they went on to write many series, including *Cardcaptor Sakura* and *Chobits*, two of the most popular manga in the United States. Like many Japanese manga artists, they prefer to avoid the spotlight, and little is known about them personally.

CLAMP is currently publishing three series in Japan: *Tsubasa* and *xxxHOLiC* with Kodansha and *Gohou Drug* with Kadokawa.

Translation Notes

Japanese is a tricky language for most Westerners, and translation is often more art than science. For your edification and reading pleasure, here are notes on some of the places where we could have gone in a different direction in our translation of the work, or where a Japanese cultural reference is used.

Tora-Cola

If you will remember from the previous volume, "Tora" means Tiger—the mascot of Osaka's baseball team, the Hanshin Tigers, and the symbol of the entire Hanshin Republic. History buffs might also recognize "Tora" as the Japanese Navy's signal to start the attack on Pearl Harbor: "Tora Tora Tora."

Chu'nyan

What's with the apostrophe? It's just to note that the n belongs with "nyan" rather than with "Chu." By the way, "chu" uses the kanji (the Japanese system of writing) for "spring," and "nyan" uses the kanji for "scent."

Ryanban

The "Ry" combination is one of the most difficult combination of sounds for native, monolingual English speakers to wrap their lips around. Many would pronounce "Ryan" as if they were saying the first name of Ryan O'Neal. Not quite. First, remember that the "r"

193

sound in Japanese sounds like a very light "d" sound—similar to the "r" sound that an upper-class British person would use to pronounce the word "very." Add that to a "ya" sound, and you get a single syllable that sounds a little like "dya." Remember, it's not "di-ya" or "ri-ya," but "rya."

Manju

The same type of big, white, wheat-dough bun as Siu Bao found in dim sum restaurants, and sometimes sold steaming hot on a chilly autumn day by street vendors in Yokohama's Chinatown. Mmmm.

Mito Kômon

One of Japan's most popular hour-long TV dramas, "Mito Kômon" began its run in 1970 and continues today. The main character is an elderly aristocrat who travels Japan with his three retainers, finding injustice and doing what he can to correct it. In the last act of every show, just when the bad guys seem to have the upper hand (reportedly at exactly the same minute mark of every program), Mito-sama pulls out the emblem of his nephew, the Shogun! The bad guys

realize that Mito-sama's influence trumps any power they might have, and they capitulate. Like James Bond, the title character has been played by a number of different actors.

Rowing the Boat or Asleep at the Oar

Actually, both of these phrases mean the same thing . . . that Sakura is basically asleep. "Asleep at the oar" is obvious, but "rowing the boat" also means that she's a little brain-numb—probably because of the less-than-towering amount of brain work it takes to row.

Gambling Prizes

Cash payoffs for gambling are illegal in Japan, so you will find that gambling for prizes is a very normal occurrence. Unlike skeeball-style amusement centers in the U.S., the prize counters at pachinko parlors are more like mini convenience stores with food, cigarettes, and household items. In Chu'nyan's country the prizes are a natural product of the barter system, and bringing home groceries from your lucky gambling trip is very common to Japanese readers.

Moxibustion

An ancient Chinese remedy, possibly even the precursor to acupuncture, since the Chinese word for acupuncture literally means "acupuncture-moxibustion." A lit and smoldering stick of mugwort is placed on or over an acupuncture point (sometimes to the point of scarring the skin). When combined with acupuncture, the lit mugwort is attached to heat the needle. Like most Chinese medicine, the purpose of moxibustion is to enhance the blood flow and elevate the chi. The Kiishim intends to treat Kurogane and Fai with a full-body acid-based moxibustion, which would almost assuredly be . . . unpleasant.

Mirrors

Mirrors are a traditional mystic element of the earliest parts of Japanese culture. According to

the Kojiki (the book of Japanese myths), the Sun Goddess Amaterasu ordered her son, Ninigi-no-Mikoto, to go to Earth, and with him she sent three sacred objects: a magatama (a beadlike jewel accessory), a sword, and a mirror. Those three objects have been passed down in the Japanese imperial family. Mystical mirrors have also crept into Japan's fox-spirit tales and other traditional stories.

Preview of Volume 4

Here is an excerpt from Volume 4, on sale in English now.

よくも私をこんな城に閉じこめてくれたな

ひっ

この領主は私が預かろう

……ゆっくり礼をせねばならん

信用しても大丈夫そうだよ——その秘妖さん

い…いやだ!!

ジタバタ

おまえの母親は
良い秘術師（シバン）だった

この領主（リヤンバン）の
卑劣（ひれつ）な罠（わな）によって
亡（な）きものとなったが

私（わたし）との戦（たたか）いで
己（おのれ）を磨（みが）き

おまえが成長（せいちょう）して
そんな己（おのれ）以上（いじょう）の秘術師（シバン）に
なることを楽（たの）しみにしている
と言（い）っていた

TOMARE!

[STOP!]

You're going the wrong way!

Manga is a completely different type of reading experience.

To start at the *beginning*,
go to the *end*!

That's right! Authentic manga is read the traditional Japanese way—from right to left. Exactly the *opposite* of how American books are read. It's easy to follow: Just go to the other end of the book, and read each page—and each panel—from right side to left side, starting at the top right. Now you're experiencing manga as it was meant to be.